CHEMICAL ENERGY

Selected Topics in Modern Chemistry

SERIES EDITORS

Professor Harry H. Sisler
University of Florida
Gainesville, Florida

Professor Calvin A. VanderWerf
Hope College
Holland, Michigan

Series Editors' Statement

AN OUTSTANDING development in recent college chemistry curricula has been a greatly increased emphasis on thermodynamic principles in the elementary college course. This new addition to Reinhold's SELECTED TOPICS IN MODERN CHEMISTRY has been prepared by two leaders in the field of chemical education who were in the vanguard of those who advocated this development. As a result, they brought to the task of preparing this volume a wealth of experience and "know-how" in the presentation of the principles of chemical thermodynamics to elementary students.

"Chemical Energy" is a readable, authoritative, and thoroughly modern addition to the literature of chemical education. It will, we believe, be thoroughly enjoyed by both teacher and student.

HARRY H. SISLER
CALVIN A. VANDERWERF

CHEMICAL ENERGY

LAURENCE E. STRONG

Professor of Chemistry

and

WILMER J. STRATTON

Associate Professor of Chemistry
Earlham College
Richmond, Indiana

New York

REINHOLD   PUBLISHING   CORPORATION

Chapman & Hall Ltd., London

PREFACE

ONE OF the cornerstones of modern physical science is the study of energy and the processes by which it is transferred as heat and work. Commonly referred to as *thermodynamics*, this discipline was first developed to provide a better understanding of heat engines. However, the principles which emerged have been found to be remarkably general and to provide a powerful tool for analyzing changes of all kinds. Our particular interest in this book is with the association between chemical change and energy; thus the title, "Chemical Energy."

Thermodynamics is an elegantly logical subject. Probably no other aspect of modern science is an elegant and yet so straightforward. Applied to chemical reactions, we find it an intriguing subject, not only because of its logic but also because of the new vistas that appear as various chemical systems are examined in the light of thermodynamic principles. This small volume attempts to paint a few of these vistas. If the reader becomes sufficiently intrigued to look further—to examine additional systems and to discover new vistas on his own—then we shall have succeeded in our purpose.

The core of this book is the application of the concepts of energy and entropy to the interpretation of chemical change. The bulk of the theoretical discussion is in Chapters 1, 2, and 5, with computational procedures discussed in Chapters 3 and 6. Chapters 4 and 7 are then devoted to application of the basic concepts to the study of a variety of chemical systems. We consider Chapters 4 and 7 to be the heart of the subject for chemists and these are for us the parts which provide the greatest fascination.

Any serious study of chemical thermodynamics almost certainly requires that the student grapple with problems and calculations on his own. Limitations of space and the introductory nature of this volume have forced us to omit most of the problems we would otherwise include. Many textbooks of physical chemistry include extensive collections of problems, which can be quite helpful.

The book has been written at a level which we hope will make it useful and stimulating for first year college chemistry students. Mathematics has been used sparingly, with only a knowledge of college algebra being required. In our own teaching, an expanded version of this book serves as the focus for a one-term second year course in elementary chemical thermodynamics. We supplement this material with numerous problem assignments, with more extensive exposure to such topics as electro-analytical chemistry, and with appropriate laboratory investigations using the techniques of calorimetry, potentiometry, and equilibrium measurements.

We are indebted to a number of people for helpful suggestions and for stimulating our thinking in new directions. We would like especially to express appreciation to our colleagues Theodor Benfey and Gerald Bakker for reading the first draft of the manuscript and making many valuable suggestions. The discussion of entropy and free energy in Chapter 5 has grown out of conversations with Professor Frank Halliwell of the University of North Staffordshire in England. Finally, any student of thermodynamics cannot help but be in debt to G. N. Lewis and M. Randall for their classic book on thermodynamics, a book now available in an edition prepared by K. S. Pitzer and L. Brewer and published by McGraw-Hill Book Company in 1961.

LAURENCE E. STRONG
WILMER J. STRATTON

CONTENTS

SYMBOLS AND
ABBREVIATIONS

aq	aqueous solution
atm	atmosphere
C	concentration
cal	calorie
deg	degree (Celsius or Kelvin)
Δ	change from state 1 to state 2
E	internal energy
$\mathcal{E}$	potential difference (voltage)
F	Faraday constant (96,500 coulombs/mole of electrons)
g	gas phase
G	free energy
H	enthalpy
$\mathbf{k}$	Boltzmann constant
K	equilibrium constant
kcal	kilocalorie
l	liquid phase
M	molarity (moles/liter)
n	number of moles
$\mathcal{N}$	Avogadro's number (6.02×10^{23} units/mole)
P	pressure
$Q\ (q)$	heat
R	gas constant (1.987 cal/deg-mole)
s	solid phase
S	entropy
T	absolute temperature (Kelvin scale)
V	volume
$W\ (w)$	work

INTERCONNECTIONS
AMONG CHANGES

FROM THE earliest records of man's activities fire has played a significant role. Fires have been used not only to change the temperature of objects but also to alter objects in other ways. Thus the cooking of foods has long been known to involve more than merely a temperature change. Just what the connection is between a fire and the changes produced in other objects has been subject to many interpretations. An early view described fire as a source of heat. Aristotle described heat or fire as one of the four essential qualities characteristic of all objects. By the 18th century fire was considered to release a substance called "caloric." Lavoisier, in his textbook published in 1789, included this as one of the chemical elements. It remained for Lord Kelvin and Joule to work out an experimental basis for relating heat to work, and to argue that neither one is in any way to be identified as a chemical element but rather as different aspects of something called energy. Further investigations by many scientists led to the formulation of the energetics of chemical reaction systems. It is this formulation that is to be discussed in this book.

Before limiting the discussion to the chemical aspects of energy, some of its general features should be pointed out.

These will serve not only to fit the discussion into a larger context, but also to provide tools with which it is possible to carry on various laboratory investigations.

1-1.   Temperature-Changing Capacity

Suppose that a weight of 50 kilograms were dropped from a ten-story building and fell 30 meters into a tub containing 10 liters of water at 20°C; and also suppose that the resulting splash were confined so that no water escaped from the tub. In such a case, experiments show that the temperature of the water would rise by about 0.3°C.

Such experiments are difficult to carry out. However, a related experiment can be easily performed. If a Thermos bottle is partially filled with water, a reasonably sensitive thermometer immersed in the water, and the bottle then stoppered, this provides a system quite analogous to the weight, the building, and the water tub, but a bit easier to work with. When the Thermos bottle is shaken rapidly up and down, the thermometer indicates a rise in temperature. In a typical experiment the temperature of the water is found to rise approximately 0.6°C during 10 minutes of shaking. It seems reasonable to conclude that this increase in temperature results from the energy of the impact of the water as it is suddenly stopped by the bottle walls at each cycle of the shaking.

There are other ways of changing the temperature of water. If two samples of water initially at different temperatures are poured simultaneously into a Thermos bottle, the final temperature of the contents of the bottle is different from either initial temperature. Here the final temperature is always somewhere between the temperature of the two different portions of water.

Actually the same results can be obtained, so far as temperature changes are concerned, when the samples are separated by a partition of sheet metal or other material. With this arrangement we say that **heat** is transferred through the partition from the warmer to the colder sample. It is also customary to extend the same idea of heat transfer to the systems produced by actual mixing. For two water samples initially at the same temperature there is no temperature change upon mixing.

When separate solutions of the two reagents hydrochloric acid and sodium hydroxide, each at 25°C, are mixed, the final temperature is higher than the initial temperature. For a fixed amount of the two reagents the magnitude of the temperature increase also depends upon the amount of water present; the smaller the amount of water the greater the temperature increase. For a given total amount of solution but different ratios of the two reagents, results can be obtained such as those plotted in Fig. 1-1. These data indicate that the temperature rise is determined by the relative amounts of the two materials. For one particular mole ratio of the two materials, a greater rise is observed than for any other mole ratio. With hydrochloric acid and sodium hydroxide, this critical ratio is at 1 mole HCl per mole NaOH.

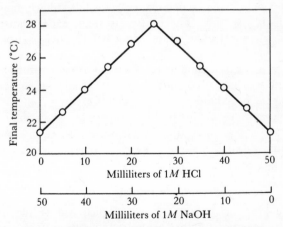

Fig. 1–1. Temperatures produced when solutions of HCl and NaOH are mixed in various mole ratios.

The critical ratio for these two substances is the same regardless of the amount of water present.

Systems with a temperature-changing capacity can be divided into two sets. For one set, exemplified by mixing hot and cold water, the temperature-changing capacity depends on the initial temperature difference. In this set the systems will undergo temperature change when mixed or when brought into contact through a separating partition. The second set, exemplified by the mixing of hydrochloric acid and sodium hydroxide, has a temperature-changing capacity even when all components of the system are initially at the same temperature. For this set a temperature change will occur only if the components are mixed together directly. Experimentally, it is also found that the final composition of each system in the second set is always different from the initial composition. They are generally classified, therefore, as chemical systems.

For temperature changes produced with water samples at different temperatures, actual mixing of the samples is not essential. For systems like hydrochloric acid and sodium hydroxide, in which chemical reaction takes place, however, mixing is essential. The possibility that heat is transferred in the chemical case is not immediately obvious from the experimental evidence. In any event, once the reaction has occurred, the system in its final state at a temperature higher than it was initially could transfer heat to another system still at the initial temperature.

Before discussing further the temperature-changing capacity of a system in relation to chemical change and to heat transfer, we shall examine a few other types of systems which exhibit capacities for change.

1-2. Capacity to Produce Electricity

If a piece of silk and a piece of glass rod or plastic are pressed together and then separated, the separated materials possess an attractive force toward each other and toward bits of paper or other small objects. Although vigorous rubbing enhances the effect, experiments suggest that only contact and separation are essential. After treatment in this way the glass and the silk are said to be electrically charged.

Such observations are interpreted by the idea that the silk and the glass become oppositely charged. When they are again placed together, the attractive forces disappear, and the charges are said to have neutralized each other. Several different pairs of materials exhibit this phenomenon of charge separation. Since rubbing is usually used, the phenomenon is often referred to as **frictional electricity.**

Frictional electricity can be compared with what at first sight appears to be a quite different phenomenon. When a zinc plate and a copper plate are placed in an aqueous solution of sodium chloride, they become electrically charged. To produce the effect it is essential that the two metals *not* touch each other, but that they be in the same solution. A stack or pile of metal plates can intensify the effect. Thus if a number of alternate zinc and copper plates are individually separated by a cloth or paper soaked in sodium chloride solution, the plates at the ends of the pile will exhibit electrical effects of quite impressive magnitude. Originally developed by an Italian scientist, Alessandro Volta, in 1800, such an arrangement is usually called a voltaic pile.

If the plates at opposite ends of a voltaic pile are connected by a wire, electric charges flow through the wire and charge neutralization takes place. Along with this charge neutralization, the zinc plates are found to decrease in mass and new substances appear in the solution. In other words, chemical changes are found to occur within the assembly of plates and solution at the same time that charge neutralization takes place along the external wire. If the wire is removed, the chemical change ceases and, conversely, anything which interferes with the chemical reaction interrupts the charge separation process.

Many other assemblies of metals and solutions produce

separated electric charges. The electric charges, once separated, are capable of inducing a variety of effects in other systems. One of these effects is temperature change. If the charges flow through a wire, the wire increases in temperature. Wires of high resistance are commonly used in this way to transfer heat to other objects. This result indicates that a system of separated charges, produced either by chemical change or friction, has a temperature-changing capacity.

1-3. Capacity to Lift Masses

Suppose that a massive object falls from a shelf to the floor. If the object is connected by a rope to a second object, the fall of the first object can cause the second object to rise. In general, one can conclude that a mass suspended above the earth possesses a capacity to lift other masses from the earth.

In Sec. 1-1 it was pointed out that a massive object which falls into water produces a temperature rise. Objects elevated above the earth, then, have both a temperature-changing and a mass-lifting capacity. If the object falls, it simultaneously loses both these capacities, even though only one may be exhibited. Indeed, it cannot lose one without the other.

The lifting of masses is a special case of the more general phenomenon of change in motion. When an object undergoes a change in elevation, a change in motion is involved. Objects may also be pushed or pulled horizontally, in which case change of motion is also a factor. There are still other ways in which motion can be produced or altered.

Some chemical reactions can be carried out in such a way as to produce motion, including the lifting of masses. If a piece of zinc is dropped into hydrochloric acid, hydrogen gas is evolved which expands to occupy a volume many times larger than the starting materials. Expanding gases can be used to produce motion, as in a jet engine, or can push against a piston which is connected to some kind of mechanical device.

Most impressive is the behavior of animal muscles. Here a large number of different chemicals are present and the chemical changes are complex, but they result in motion and the ability to lift masses. Plants also offer impressive demonstrations of motion changes. A giant redwood tree in a year's time lifts many tons of water from its roots to its leaves, where the water evaporates into the air. This water transport process continues only so long as the chemical reactions within the cells of the tree continue.

The ability of a system to change the motion of other objects, even when forces are operating to prevent the motion, is a general phenomenon. Physicists usually refer to this ability as the capacity to do **work.**

1-4. The Capacity to Produce Light

Whenever a solid object is raised in temperature to 600°C or higher, it will glow visibly. As the temperature rises, the glow becomes more intense. The temperature rise can be produced by friction, by electricity, or by chemical change. On the other hand, a number of animals and plants are found to glow without being at a high temperature. The firefly is the most conspicuous example of this phenomenon. A few chemical systems simpler than plants and animals also glow at room temperature. The chemical called luminol reacts with oxygen,[1] and the whole system glows with sufficient intensity to affect not only the eyes but also light meters and photographic film.

1-5. The Interconnection of Changes

A summary of the various systems and their capacities as discussed thus far is shown in Table 1-1.

[1] E. H. White, *J. Chem. Educ.*, **34,** 275 (1957).

TABLE 1-1. A Summary of Interconnected Changes

System	Capacity to Produce	Characteristic Process
Elevated object	Heat	Elevation change coupled to temperature change
Chemicals	Heat	Composition change or phase change coupled to temperature change
Cloth and glass	Electricity	Separation after contact coupled to charge changes
Metal plates and solution	Electricity	Chemical change coupled to charge changes
Elevated object	Work	Elevation decrease coupled to elevation increase
Chemicals	Work	Chemical change coupled to elevation change
Hot object	Light	Temperature decrease coupled to temperature increase at a distance
Chemicals	Light	Chemical change coupled to temperature change at a distance

In all these cases, each particular capacity can be exhibited when the one system is connected to some second system called a detector. This second system may, for example, be a tub of water for heat; a coil of wire and a tub of water for electricity; a friction device and a tub of water for work; a dull, black object and a tub of water for light. The diverse systems can each lead to the same result when suitably connected to a tub of water, namely, a rise in the temperature of the water. On this experimental basis they are all said to be interconnected.

What are the properties of this interconnection? Quantitative experiments show that a given change in a system will produce only a certain amount of change in a second system. These quantitative aspects are quite accurately reproducible. The reproducibility in the magnitude of coupled changes can be taken to imply that *there is some feature of the coupling that remains fixed or invariant.* Another way of expressing the feature of reproducibility is to say that within the changes something is conserved. Put in this way, we almost automatically ask, "What is conserved when changes are interconnected?"

It is clear that whatever the something may be, it is never a material object. But to call it simply "something that is conserved" seems rather awkward. It is customary therefore to apply the name **energy** to that which is conserved during changes. When interconnected systems undergo changes, we say that energy is transferred from the one system to the other, but remains unchanged in amount. Such an identification of energy as nothing more nor less than a concept may seem a bit insubstantial at first sight. It has proved through the years, however, to be an amazingly effective idea for interpreting phenomena.

Each of the phenomena described earlier can be interpreted as an example of energy being transferred from one system to another. Table 1-2 suggests the relationships.

TABLE 1-2. Types of Energy Transfer

Common Name	Energy Designation	Condition for Transfer
Heat	Thermal energy	Temperature difference
Electricity	Electric energy	Charge difference
Work	Mechanical energy	Change in motion
Light	Radiant energy	Temperature difference

The idea that energy is something conserved during changes is not unlike that of money in a business. So long as an accountant believes that money is neither created nor destroyed, but merely transferred, he can keep a reliable and consistent set of books. In any period of time the income and outgo of money must precisely balance. If the balance cannot be found, it suggests that money is stored somewhere in the business. Of course, with money such a conclusion can often be verified by examining the cash register. When the balance fails, one suspects some human error which, in principle, can be detected, or else one introduces the notions of debits and credits to restore the conservation of money principle.

With methods for measuring energy quantitatively, the idea of energy conservation becomes of key importance. Just as with money, an accounting procedure for energy can be devised. In the remainder of this book our primary concern will be with experimental systems which involve chemical changes. To these systems we plan to apply accounting principles not only to follow the energy transfers, but also to try to deduce how and where energy may be stored in a chemical system. For this reason the book has been called "Chemical Energy."

1-6. Units of Energy

If we accept the idea that energy is conserved during any set of coupled changes, then it is possible to assign numerical units to energy and thereby develop quantitative interrelationships.

The basic unit of energy in the *cgs* system is the **erg**, while in the *mks* system it is the **joule** (1 joule = 10^7 ergs). All other units of energy are now defined by international agreement in terms of the joule.

Chemists tend to use a unit of energy called the **calorie**. Historically this was taken as the energy necessary to raise by 1°C the temperature of 1 gram of water at about 15°C. Experimentally it was found that 1 calorie was equivalent to approximately 4.18 joules of mechanical energy, and the joule is now the accepted basis for the precise definition of the calorie:

$$1 \text{ calorie} \equiv 4.1840 \text{ joules}$$

Energy changes accompanying chemical reactions are usually in the range of a few thousand calories per mole of reactants, and it is customary to express these changes in

kilocalories:

$$1 \text{ kcal} = 1000 \text{ cal} = 4.1840 \times 10^3 \text{ joules}$$

Nutritional discussions of the energy available from foods use the kilocalorie as the energy unit, although the prefix *kilo* is usually omitted, and a capital C is used.

Electric energy is one of the major forms of energy involved in chemical systems, and we shall have occasion to consider it in some detail later. It can be shown that when an electric current is allowed to flow through a circuit, the electric potential difference multiplied by the total flow of electric charge is equal to the electric potential energy change. The unit of electric charge is the **coulomb** which is defined in such a way that

$$1 \text{ volt-coulomb} = 1 \text{ joule}$$

$$= 0.239 \text{ cal}$$

In measuring electric energy produced by a chemical reaction, it is important to know the total electric charge (i.e., the number of coulombs) equivalent to 1 mole of electrons. This unit, called the **faraday,** equals 96,500 coulombs per mole of electrons:

$$1 \text{ volt-faraday} = 96,500 \text{ volt-coulombs}$$

$$= 23.06 \text{ kcal}$$

Another form of energy which is important in the study of chemical reactions is the energy associated with volume changes. This will be discussed in more detail in later chapters; it is sufficient to point out here that pressure is defined as force per unit area, and therefore that

$$P \times V = (\text{force/area}) \times \text{volume} = \text{force} \times \text{distance} = \text{energy}$$

Thus $P \times V$ has the dimensions of energy. For the usual units of P and V in atmospheres and liters,

$$1 \text{ liter-atm} = 24.2 \text{ cal}$$

The gas constant, R, will be encountered in several types of energy calculations. This constant, defined by $PV = nRT$ for an ideal gas, has the dimensions of energy/degree-mole. The two descriptions of R most commonly used are:

$$R = 0.0821 \text{ liter-atm/deg-mole}$$

$$= 1.987 \text{ cal/deg-mole}$$

chapter two

TEMPERATURE–CHANGING
CAPACITY

ONE OF the conspicuous changes which chemical systems undergo is change in temperature as an accompaniment to chemical change. In the previous chapter it was pointed out that temperature differences can be the basis of the coupling of two different systems for the transfer of thermal energy. If a chemical system initially is at the same temperature as its surroundings but finally is at a different temperature, it is possible for thermal energy to be transferred from the system to the surroundings. The fact that a chemical system can change its temperature provides a means by which the system may be coupled to its surroundings. How can we describe the ability to change temperature which a chemical system may have?

2-1. Definition of Change

In all cases of temperature change as a result of chemical change the precise temperatures finally attained depend on many factors. To make such data meaningful, therefore, requires careful definition of the **system.** The word "system" refers to materials isolated for study. The isolation may be actual separation from the surroundings by means of barriers, or it may be an isolation conceived only in the mind.

A chemical system is further defined by describing the **state** of the system. Properly given, it should be possible for any-one to reproduce the system again by following the descrip-tion.

When a change is observed, the change is described by

Final state of the system − Initial state of the system = Change

It is not therefore the system that changes, but rather the *state* of the system. Although a complete description of the change must include every detail which can be observed in both the final and the initial states, experience leads chemists to devote their major attention to only a few aspects of each state. Prominent among these aspects are composition (C), pressure (P), volume (V), and temperature (T). On this basis a change in state of a chemical system may be de-scribed by

$$C_2 - C_1 = \Delta C$$
$$P_2 - P_1 = \Delta P$$
$$V_2 - V_1 = \Delta V$$
$$T_2 - T_1 = \Delta T$$

Mass is another important quantity, but chemists always deal with systems so chosen that the total mass remains con-stant, at least within the error of experiment.

If a chemical system undergoes a reaction there is a change in composition, so that $C_2 - C_1 \neq 0$. Placed in an open con-tainer in the laboratory, a system will be under the pressure of the atmosphere. Since this pressure is substantially con-stant, at least over a period of a few minutes and often even a few hours, it is reasonable to specify that $P_2 - P_1 = 0$. Once the pressure is fixed, it is usually not feasible to insist that the volume remain fixed; therefore $V_2 - V_1 \neq 0$. Alter-natively, the volume may be held constant, in which case $V_2 - V_1 = 0$ but $P_2 - P_1 \neq 0$.

Many common reaction systems have a final temperature higher than the initial temperature. Let us therefore restrict the discussion to the case where $T_2 - T_1 > 0$. This implies that for each system to be studied we wish to know the highest final temperature that can be reached from some chosen initial temperature. To get such data requires that the system be uncoupled from its surroundings so that no thermal energy is transferred out of it.

A system which changes but is unable to transfer thermal energy is said to change by an **adiabatic process.** An adiabatic process can be achieved either by surrounding the system with an insulating blanket, or by altering the temperature of the surroundings so that no temperature difference ever exists between the surroundings and the system. With proper precautions it is possible to obtain reproducible temperature data, although precise definition of the system is often difficult.

There is an alternate strategy for studying a chemical change. Instead of isolating the system by thermal insulation and then measuring the temperature change that accompanies a chemical change, the chemical change can be carried out in such a way that the temperature remains constant. A process for which $\Delta T = 0$ is called an **isothermal process.** If the reaction system tends to increase in temperature, it can be placed in contact with a water bath whose temperature is slightly below that of the reaction system. As the reaction proceeds, the water bath is observed to rise in temperature as thermal energy is transferred to it from the chemical system. If proper conditions are chosen, the final temperature will be close to what the system was initially. From knowledge of the mass of the water bath and its temperature change, it is possible to calculate the amount of thermal energy transferred out of the chemical system.

2-2. Internal Energy

Adiabatic and isothermal processes present two extreme possibilities for conducting a chemical reaction. In both processes the chemical reaction which takes place can be essentially the same, but the effects on the surroundings are quite different. In one case a rise in the temperature of the system is observed ($\Delta T > 0$) but no energy leaves the system ($Q = 0$); in the other case the temperature remains constant ($\Delta T = 0$) but thermal energy (Q) is transferred to the surroundings. If the chemical change takes place at constant volume, then the transfer of thermal energy for the isothermal process is denoted by Q_v, where the subscript v indicates constant volume.

The obvious question concerning the isothermal process is, "Where did the thermal energy come from?" Since energy has been defined as something whose total quantity remains unchanged, it must be concluded that the system in its initial state contains energy other than thermal energy, and that the latter appears entirely at the expense of these other forms. Let us therefore introduce a new symbol, E, to describe the energy a system possesses. This energy, E, is a function of the state of the system, and it is defined in such a way that, when a change in the state of the system occurs at constant temperatures,

$$E_2 - E_1 = \Delta E = Q_v \qquad (2\text{-}1)$$

For an adiabatic process, no thermal energy leaves the system ($Q = 0$), and thus from the law of conservation of energy the energy within the system must remain constant, or

$$\Delta E = 0$$

Because the quantity E is a measure of the energy within a system it is usually called **internal energy.**

So far we have limited the discussion to the cases where a system transfers energy to the surroundings in the form of thermal energy, or heat. Energy transfer may also take other forms, as discussed in Chapter 1. In particular, chemical systems may transfer mechanical energy as a result of volume change, or, with the proper apparatus, they may transfer large amounts of electric energy. In common usage, both of these are called work, and are described by the symbol W. But if energy can be transferred out of a system in the form of work, as well as heat, then the internal energy of the system must decrease by an amount $(Q + W)$. (The subscript v is no longer applicable since work due to volume change is included.) Therefore a more general statement of the law of conservation of energy is given by Eq. (2-2).

$$\Delta E = Q + W \qquad (2\text{-}2)$$

This important generalization is usually referred to as the **First Law of Thermodynamics.** For both Q and W a positive sign is understood to indicate a transfer of energy into the system, while a negative sign indicates energy transferred out of the system. A positive sign for ΔE thus indicates a rise in the internal energy of the system, and a negative sign indicates a decrease.[1]

Chemical changes are frequently carried out by the direct mixing of reagents in an open container. When this is the case no electric work is transferred, and the only possible work is that associated with volume change. If a system expands its volume by an amount ΔV and at the same time pushes against an external pressure, P_{ext}, it does work on the surroundings equal to $P\Delta V$. Conversely, if the volume of the system decreases, then work will be transferred from the surroundings to the system. Work is defined as positive for energy added to the system, thus

$$W = -P_{ext}\Delta V \qquad (2\text{-}3)$$

If work due to volume change is the only work transferred, then Eq. (2-2) becomes

$$\Delta E = Q - P_{ext}\Delta V \qquad (2\text{-}4)$$

[1] In some books the quantity, W, is given a positive sign for work transferred out of the system. With this sign convention $\Delta E = Q - W$ and $W = +P\Delta V$. However, it seems preferable to identify with a positive sign all energies transferred into a system.

If we now impose the restriction of a change at constant volume, we see that $P_{ext} \Delta V = 0$, and therefore that

$$\Delta E = Q_v \qquad (2\text{-}1)$$

Thus Eq. (2-1) is a special case of the more general relationship, Eq. (2-2).

2-3. Enthalpy

Chemical reactions may be carried out in the laboratory under conditions of constant volume by using a closed container with rigid walls. Much more common, however, is the situation where reaction takes place in an open container. A system which is open to the atmosphere must be at atmospheric pressure; otherwise the imbalance of forces would result in a tendency to expand or contract. When a chemical change takes place in contact with the atmosphere, the volume will change, but in such a way that the final pressure of the system equals the atmospheric pressure. Since atmospheric pressure does not change significantly over a period of hours, a reaction in an open container may be considered to be a constant-pressure process.

If the pressure of a system, P, equals the external pressure, P_{ext}, then substituting in Eq. (2-4) for the case of a constant-pressure process gives

$$\Delta E = Q_p - P\Delta V$$

Rearranging and expanding gives

$$Q_p = E + P\Delta V$$
$$= E_2 - E_1 + P(V_2 - V_1)$$

Collecting terms for the initial and final states gives

$$Q_p = (E_2 + PV_2) - (E_1 + PV_1) \qquad (2\text{-}5)$$

Since reaction at constant pressure is the most common situation in the laboratory, Eq. (2-5) suggests that the quantity

$(E + PV)$ is an important one. The product PV has the dimensions of energy (Sec. 1-6); thus $(E + PV)$ also has the dimensions of energy. If we define a new function, H, such that

$$H \equiv E + PV \qquad (2\text{-}6)$$

then Eq. (2-5) becomes

$$Q_p = H_2 - H_1$$

or

$$Q_p = \Delta H \qquad (2\text{-}7)$$

Thus the change in the function H equals the thermal energy transfer between the system and its surroundings for a process at constant pressure. Eq. (2-1) shows that ΔE is the corresponding quantity for a process at constant volume.

Various names have been used for the energy function which we have identified with the symbol H. At one time it was called heat content, but this unfortunately implies that a system stores energy as heat, whereas heat has been defined as energy being transferred. It is sometimes called total energy to indicate that it is made up of the internal energy, E, plus an "external energy" which a system possesses by virtue of occupying a volume, V, at a pressure, P. A more widely used term for H is **enthalpy**. This is really just a Greek term meaning "heat content," but we shall use it, in keeping with the common convention.[2]

Having now introduced two functions, ΔE and ΔH, to describe the energetics of a chemical change, we wish to know how the two functions are related and by how much they differ. From Eq. (2-6) it can be shown that, at constant pressure,

$$\Delta H = \Delta E + P\Delta V \qquad (2\text{-}8)$$

---

[2] Although enthalpy has the dimensions of energy, it is not, strictly speaking, an energy, because it can be shown that under certain circumstances enthalpy is not conserved. In practice, however, it would appear that no great injustice is done by considering enthalpy to be an energy function.

TABLE 2-1. Enthalpy and Internal Energy Changes for Typical Chemical Reactions at 25°C and 1 atm

System	ΔH (kcal)	ΔV (liter)	ΔE, Calc'd (kcal)
$H_2(g) + \frac{1}{2}O_2(g) \rightarrow H_2O(l)$	-68.32	-36.7	-67.43
$\frac{1}{2}N_2(g) + \frac{3}{2}H_2(g) \rightarrow NH_3(g)$	-11.04	-24.5	-10.49
$NaOH(1M) + HCl(1M) \rightarrow NaCl(\frac{1}{2}M) + H_2O(l)$	-13.84	$+0.025$	-13.84
$CuSO_4(s) + 5H_2O(l) \rightarrow \quad CuSO_4 \cdot 5H_2O(s)$	-18.85	-0.025	-18.85

thus the difference $(\Delta H - \Delta E)$ is simply $P\Delta V$. Data for some typical chemical reactions are presented in Table 2-1. The values of ΔH, and ΔV, and ΔE are given for the molar quantities shown in the equations. Experimental density values have been used to calculate ΔV at a constant pressure of 1 atm. The right-hand column lists values of ΔE calculated by means of Eq. (2-8) and the conversion factor 24.2 cal/liter-atm. The significant thing to observe in this table is that the numerical difference between ΔH and ΔE is really quite small and in some cases negligible. As a general rule, the difference between ΔH and ΔE is negligible for reactions which do not involve any gaseous components.

2-4. Calorimetry

Before proceeding further with the development of chemical energy concepts, let us examine briefly the ways in which energy data are obtained experimentally. Two ways of observing the energy effects in chemical reactions were described in Sec. 2-1: (1) measurement of temperature change at constant energy (adiabatic process), and (2) measurement of energy transfer at constant temperature (isothermal process). The usual experimental method for determining ΔH or ΔE is, in a sense, intermediate between these two extremes. A reaction is carried out in thermal contact with a water bath, but the whole apparatus—system plus water bath—is insulated to prevent any heat transfer to the larger environment. Thus the entire apparatus is held at constant energy and undergoes a temperature change; on the other hand, the quantity of reactants and size of the water bath are chosen so that only a small, easily-measured temperature change is produced. The apparatus for such measurements is called a **calorimeter**.

A simple version of a constant-pressure calorimeter is shown in Fig. 2-1. For precise work, the apparatus is often

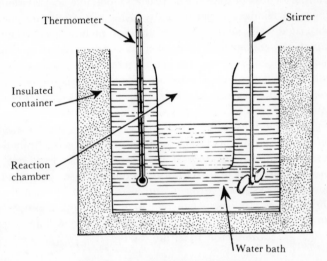

Fig. 2–1. Constant pressure calorimeter.

considerably more complex, although the fundamental design is the same as in Fig. 2-1.[3] From the observed temperature change, plus a knowledge of the heat required to raise or lower the temperature of the total apparatus by a

[3] A good discussion of calorimetry is found in the recent book by C. T. Mortimer, "Reaction Heats and Bond Strengths," Pergamon Press, 1962, pp. 15–25. (Distributed by Addison-Wesley Publishing Co., Reading, Mass.) See also G. T. Armstrong, *J. Chem. Educ.*, **41,** 297 (1964).

fixed amount, it is possible to calculate the energy that would have to be transferred to restore the whole apparatus to its initial temperature. This computed energy, Q_p, is then the desired enthalpy change, ΔH.

The preceding discussion has described procedures for calorimetric studies at constant pressure, using a container which is open to the atmosphere. (By "open" is meant subject to external pressure, but not necessarily open to heat transfer or loss of material.) It is also possible to carry out chemical changes experimentally using a closed container with rigid walls, so that if the system completely fills the container, the change will take place at constant volume. For most chemical systems this requirement of a fixed volume will result in a change of pressure. Since the pressure change may be quite large, it is necessary to use a heavy steel container designed to withstand such changes without deforming or exploding. The apparatus is usually called a *bomb calorimeter*, as any enclosed pressure vessel is technically termed a bomb. This type of apparatus has been extensively used for the study of oxidation reactions because compounds containing carbon, hydrogen, and nitrogen can be burned in the presence of oxygen with relative ease. Using a properly designed bomb calorimeter, it is possible to obtain data which are reproducible to within $\pm 0.05\%$.[3]

2-5. Molecular Interpretation of Internal Energy

In Sec. 2-2 the energy symbolized by E was referred to as internal energy. Internal energy can be regarded as made up of several terms.

$$E = E_0 + E_{elec} + E_{trans} + E_{vib} + E_{rot} \tag{2-9}$$

All the parts except E_0 can be imagined to arise from the interrelationship of nuclei and electrons. E_{elec} is the sum of the electric potential energy of interaction between nuclei and electrons, both within and between atoms, and the kinetic energy of electrons. The last three terms are the energies associated with the various types of nuclear motion: translation or movement of the total molecule, vibration of the various nuclei with respect to one another, and rotation about one or more axes in the molecule. Each particle, no matter how simple or complex, can be considered to have three directions of translational motion for the particle as a whole, while the number of vibrational and rotational motions depends on the molecular complexity. It is these three forms of motion taken together (translation, vibration, and rotation) which comprise the kinetic energy of a system. Each one has a definite value, but all are proportional to the absolute temperature of the system.[4]

The E_0 term will include still other energies related to nuclear interactions, to the interaction between the system and fields of force such as gravitational fields, and to other energies which may not now be known. Only in a formal sense can the internal energy of any system be considered truly internal. In practice in a terrestrial laboratory, however, energy changes related to external fields of force are so small or so nearly constant that they can usually be neglected. Systems for which they cannot be neglected include high-speed centrifugation, large changes in distance from the earth's center, powerful heterogeneous magnetic fields, and powerful heterogeneous electric fields.

It is the E_{elec} term that is usually of most interest in chem-

---

[4] Strictly speaking, these energies are quantized, so that there is not a simple, proportional relationship between energy and temperature. The energies increase with increasing temperature, but only in discrete steps. However at ordinary temperatures the quantization of translation and rotation energies is negligible, while vibration energies contribute relatively little to the total energy of a substance. For an excellent discussion of energy and internal molecular motion, see Barrow, "Physical Chemistry," McGraw-Hill, New York, 1961, pp. 77–82, 122–125.

ical reactions. For polyelectronic atoms this term is a large negative quantity; however, only relatively small changes occur during chemical reactions. Chemical changes involve rearrangements between atoms, i.e., the making and breaking of chemical bonds, and it is the electric potential energy changes associated with these bond changes that is used to account for the major energy change.

2-6. Summary

In this chapter the groundwork has been laid for an understanding of the ways in which energy changes for chemical systems can be studied. Several possible restrictions for chemical changes—adiabatic, isothermal, constant pressure, and constant volume—have been introduced, as well as two functions to describe the energy of a chemical system—internal energy and enthalpy. In the next chapter we shall discuss some of the conventions used in calculating energy changes and some methods for indirect determination of reaction energies. The internal energy, E, and the enthalpy, H, both appear to be suitable measures of the energy of a chemical system. Changes in either one can be measured by direct experimental techniques: ΔE in a constant-volume calorimeter and ΔH in a constant-pressure calorimeter. However, it will simplify later calculations and tabulations of data if one of these is used for all data. Since H is the conventionally preferred quantity, it will be used in the following discussion of reaction energies.

chapter three

THE ARITHMETIC
OF ENERGY

THE EXCHANGE of thermal energy between a chemical system and its surroundings can be measured with precision for many reactions. In the previous chapter it was suggested that energy transfer data can be related to the internal structural features of a system and to chemical reactivity. Although some systems lend themselves readily to thermal energy measurements, there are, unfortunately, many others which do not. Thus it is relatively easy to get data for the system

$$H_2 + \tfrac{1}{2}O_2 \rightarrow H_2O$$

but direct measurements for

$$H_2 + O_2 \rightarrow H_2O_2$$

seem to be impossible. No conditions are known for which hydrogen and oxygen unite so as to form hydrogen peroxide exclusively. Nor does anyone know how to produce the reverse reaction

$$H_2O_2 \rightarrow H_2 + O_2$$

free from other competing reactions. Without such knowledge calorimetric investigations of this reaction are fruitless.

If a systematic exploration is to be made of the enthalpy changes which attend chemical reactions, some way is needed by which data can be obtained for the many cases which do not lend themselves to direct measurement. Is there a way of proceeding so that data available for certain systems can be applied to the calculation of data for other systems? This chapter is directed to answering this question.

3-1. Specification of Thermochemical Change

Before dealing directly with the main question it is necessary to develop a procedure for accurately describing a chemical change. Only in this way will it be possible to identify energy data with the appropriate chemical reaction system. We shall indicate enthalpy changes in chemical reactions with a ΔH term beside the chemical equation. Since the enthalpy change of a reaction is known to depend on whether the component substances are solids, liquids, gases or in aqueous solution, it becomes important to specify the phase by adding the letters s, l, g, or aq after the chemical symbols in the thermochemical equation, as for example

$$H_2(g) + \tfrac{1}{2}O_2(g) \rightarrow H_2O(l) \qquad \Delta H = -68.32 \text{ kcal}^{[1]}$$

The numerical value of ΔH is the enthalpy change for reaction of the molar quantities shown in the equation. For the formation of two moles of water, ΔH would be -136.64 kcal. Note that in order to obtain the ΔH for formation of one mole of water, it is convenient to write the chemical equation using a fractional number as coefficient for O_2.

We shall find it useful to specify the temperature at which a reaction takes place, and for this a subscript number is

---

[1] All data unless otherwise indicated are taken from "Selected Values of Chemical Thermodynamic Properties," Circular of the National Bureau of Standards C500, U.S. Government Printing Office, Washington, 1952.

used, ordinarily given in degrees Kelvin (absolute temperature). Finally, it is customary to use a superscript zero if all reactants are in their **standard states,** that is if each substance is in its most stable physical form under a pressure of 1 atm and at a specified temperature, usually 25°C (298°K). (Gaseous water at 25°C is not in its standard state, but liquid water is; diamond at room temperature and atmospheric pressure is not, but graphite is.) The complete thermochemical equation for the formation of water then is

$$H_2(g) + \tfrac{1}{2}O_2(g) \longrightarrow H_2O(l) \qquad \Delta H^\circ_{298} = -68.32 \, \text{kcal}$$

This equation states that at constant temperature and pressure the formation of water from its elements liberates heat. It is said to be an **exothermic reaction** and ΔH has a negative sign. The reverse reaction, the decomposition of water into hydrogen and oxygen, absorbs heat. It is called an **endothermic reaction** and ΔH has a positive sign. Thus:

$$H_2O(l) \longrightarrow H_2(g) + \tfrac{1}{2}O_2(g) \qquad \Delta H^\circ_{298} = +68.32 \, \text{kcal}$$

For the two directions of a reaction the two enthalpy changes are found to be identical in magnitude. If this identity were not found, it would imply that the reaction, when carried through a complete cycle, could be used to transfer energy without any other over-all change in the system. Such a possibility would be a denial of the law of the conservation of energy.

3-2. Indirect Determination of Reaction Enthalpies

As suggested in the introduction to this chapter, many reactions whose enthalpy change would be of interest are not suitable for direct calorimetric study. Fortunately, an indirect method can often be used. The energy change for any process depends only on the initial and final states of the system, or

$$\Delta H = H_2 - H_1$$

This is true regardless of the intermediate steps or the way in which the change takes place. A function, such as H, which is determined only by the state of the system is called a **state function.**

Consider, for example, the reaction of magnesium oxide with dilute hydrochloric acid. If the reaction is carried out directly, the experimental result is described by:

$$MgO\,(s) + 2\,HCl\,(aq) \longrightarrow$$

$$MgCl_2\,(aq) + H_2O\,(l) \qquad \Delta H_{298} = -34.90\,kcal$$

However, the reaction can also be carried out stepwise as follows:

$$MgO\,(s) + H_2O\,(l) \longrightarrow Mg(OH)_2\,(s) \qquad \Delta H_{298} = -8.84\,kcal$$

$$Mg(OH)_2\,(s) + 2\,HCl\,(aq) \longrightarrow$$

$$MgCl_2\,(aq) + 2\,H_2O\,(l) \qquad \Delta H_{298} = \underline{-26.06\,kcal}$$
$$-34.90\,kcal$$

In the latter case, the two reaction equations can be added together algebraically so that both the over-all equation and the ΔH are identical with the first path. Thus it is seen that *thermochemical equations can be added algebraically*. This generalization is commonly known as *Hess's Law of Heat Summation*.

The relationship between these reactions can also be shown to good advantage by means of a simple diagram (Fig. 3-1). The net change is the same by either path, or

$$\Delta H_1 = \Delta H_2 + \Delta H_3$$

Going back now to the problem of the formation of hydrogen peroxide, the decomposition of hydrogen peroxide into

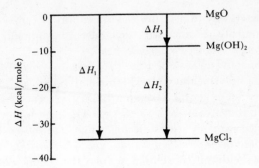

Fig. 3–1. Alternative pathways for the conversion of MgO into MgCl$_2$.

water and oxygen can be studied, giving

$$H_2O_2(l) \rightarrow H_2O(l) + \tfrac{1}{2}O_2(g) \qquad \Delta H_{298} = -23.48 \text{ kcal}$$

By reversing this equation (thereby changing the sign of ΔH) and combining it with the equation for the formation of water, we obtain

$$
\begin{array}{lll}
H_2O(l) + \tfrac{1}{2}O_2(g) & \rightarrow H_2O_2(l) & \Delta H_{298} = +23.48 \text{ kcal} \\
H_2(g) + \tfrac{1}{2}O_2(g) & \rightarrow H_2O(l) & \Delta H_{298} = -68.32 \text{ kcal} \\
\hline
H_2(g) + O_2(g) & \rightarrow H_2O_2(l) & \Delta H_{298} = -44.84 \text{ kcal}
\end{array}
$$

3-3. Enthalpy of Formation

Enthalpy changes can be determined directly or indirectly for many thousands of chemical reactions, and such information is of considerable importance to chemists. It is obviously not practical to list the values for all reactions, but some form of tabulated energy data for the compounds themselves can be the basis for the calculation of energy change for any desired reaction. There exists, we assume, a total energy per mole for each chemical substance, and such data, if available, would permit the desired calculations. Unfortunately, there is no known way to measure experimentally the total energy of a chemical substance which can give a meaningful result. *All that can be measured is a change in energy.*[2]

Fortunately there is a way to overcome this difficulty. Since the only meaningful experimental values are changes in energy, let us simply take an arbitrary reference state and assign to this a value of zero energy. The convention which chemists commonly use is the following. *The enthalpies of all pure elements in their standard state at 1 atmosphere pressure are taken to be zero.* With this convention, we may then define **enthalpy of formation** as the enthalpy change accompanying the formation of one mole of a compound from its elements. The symbol ΔH_f is used, and if all substances are in their standard states (1 atm pressure and most stable physical form) this is the standard enthalpy of formation, $\Delta H_f°$. For water at 25°C

$$H_2(g) + \tfrac{1}{2}O_2(g) \longrightarrow H_2O(l) \qquad (\Delta H_f°)_{298} = -68.32 \text{ kcal}$$

For sodium chloride at 25°C

$$Na(s) + \tfrac{1}{2}Cl_2(g) \longrightarrow NaCl(s) \qquad (\Delta H_f°)_{298} = -98.23 \text{ kcal}$$

Extensive tables of data for enthalpies of formation are available. One of the most complete is the National Bureau of Standards Circular 500, "Selected Values of Chemical

---

[2] One may argue that the Einstein equation, $E = mc^2$, gives an unequivocal measure of the energy, since all one has to do is to measure the mass of the sample. This is true, yet the energies thus calculated are so large that even the most sensitive measures of mass cannot detect the relatively small differences characteristic of chemical reactions. For example, the energy implied by the mass of 1 mole of water is about 4×10^{11} kcal, whereas the energy of chemical dissociation of water is about 200 kcal/mole. Two hundred kilocalories corresponds to a mass difference of 10^{-8} gram per mole between initial and final states. Note that the Einstein relation also indicates that the mass of a system can be kept precisely constant only so long as no energy is exchanged with other systems. It does not say that mass is converted into energy but rather that mass is transferred between coupled systems whenever energy is transferred.

Thermodynamic Properties,"[1] in which ΔH_f values along with other thermodynamic functions are tabulated for several thousand compounds. A related volume is available, giving the properties of hydrocarbons.[3] Recent editions of chemistry handbooks contain fairly extensive tables of data, taken largely from these two sources. The student should have access to one of these compilations and become familiar with its use.

Some representative enthalpies of formation are given in Table 3-1. Notice that, by definition, $\Delta H_f^{\circ} = 0$ for elements

TABLE 3-1. Standard Enthalpies of Formation, kcal/mole at 25°C and 1 atm*

Substance	ΔH_f°	Substance	ΔH_f°
$H_2(g)$	0.00	C (graphite)	0.00
$H_2O(g)$	-57.80	C (diamond)	0.45
$H_2O(l)$	-68.32	$CO(g)$	-26.42
$HCl(g)$	-22.06	$CO_2(g)$	-94.05
$KCl(s)$	-104.17	$CH_4(g)$	-17.89
S (rhombic)	0.00	$NH_3(g)$	-11.04
S (monoclinic)	0.07	$NH_4Cl(s)$	-75.38
S (g)	$+53.25$	$NO_2(g)$	8.09

* N.B.S. Circular 500.

in their most stable forms at 298°K. On the other hand, diamond and monoclinic sulfur have small positive enthalpies of formation, equal to the enthalpy of conversion into the less stable form, while gaseous sulfur has a large positive enthalpy of formation which is the energy required to vaporize the solid.

For a great many compounds the enthalpies of formation are negative. This means that heat was liberated when the compounds were formed from their elements, and thus the compounds are at a lower energy than the sum of the ener-

[3]"Selected Values of the Properties of Hydrocarbons," Circular of the National Bureau of Standards C461, U.S. Government Printing Office, Washington, 1947.

gies of the elements from which they were formed. This observation is of central importance and will be returned to later.

With data available such as that in Table 3-1, it is now possible to calculate ΔH for a great many reactions, using appropriate combinations of thermochemical equations. In practice we merely add algebraically the enthalpies of formation of the products and subtract the enthalpies of formation of the reactants.

Example. Calculate ΔH°_{298} for the reaction:

$$4\,NH_3\,(g) + 3\,O_2\,(g) \longrightarrow 2\,N_2\,(g) + 6\,H_2O\,(l)$$

$$\Delta H^\circ_{298} = 2\Delta H_f^\circ\,(N_2) + 6\Delta H_f^\circ\,(H_2O) - 4\Delta H_f^\circ\,(NH_3) - 3\Delta H_f^\circ\,(O_2)$$

Since $O_2\,(g)$ and $N_2\,(g)$ are the stable forms of pure elements at this temperature their enthalpies of formation are zero. Thus

$$\Delta H^\circ_{298} = 0 + 6(-68.32) - 4(-11.04) - 0$$

$$= -365.76 \text{ kcal}$$

3-4. Ionic Enthalpies

An important type of reaction which is commonly encountered in the laboratory is the reaction of ionic substances in aqueous solution. Consider, for example, the familiar neutralization reaction:

$$HCl\,(aq) + NaOH\,(aq) \longrightarrow H_2O\,(l) + NaCl\,(aq)$$

When this reaction is carried out using varying sets of initial concentrations of HCl and NaOH, the enthalpy change per mole of HCl and NaOH is found to be approximately constant. This is reasonable since the reaction is essentially the same regardless of the concentration. The enthalpy changes are not precisely constant, however. At low concentrations, ΔH approaches a constant value as the concentration approaches zero, while at high concentration (greater than $1M$) ΔH deviates significantly from the limiting value. If instead of HCl and NaOH, other strong acids and bases are used, the values of ΔH for the neutralization reactions in concentrated solution are found to differ slightly, but in very dilute solutions they all approach the same limiting value of -13.36 kcal/mole. These observations are consistent with present knowledge about the nature of ionic substances in aqueous solution. In the limiting case of an infinitely dilute solution the various ions are completely independent of each other, and thus it is only the hydrogen and hydroxide ions which undergo transformation. Using the symbol aq to denote the hypothetical infinitely dilute solution, we may describe the reaction most simply by

$$H^+(aq) + OH^-(aq) \longrightarrow H_2O(l) \qquad \Delta H^\circ_{298} = -13.36 \text{ kcal}$$

On the other hand, with increasing concentration, interionic attractive forces become significant, and these produce small changes in ΔH.

Since ionic equations can be simplified in this manner for dilute solutions, it would be useful to have data available for the enthalpies of formation of individual ions in solution. Unfortunately, such data are impossible to obtain, since only reactions involving compounds can be studied in the laboratory. We can determine the enthalpy of formation of an aqueous solution of HCl from the elements hydrogen and chlorine, but we cannot study an individual ion. To circumvent this dilemma, it is necessary to introduce a new reference state for ions in aqueous solution. For this purpose, *the enthalpy of formation of the hydrogen ion in dilute aqueous solution, $H^+(aq)$, at 25°C is arbitrarily set equal to zero.* With this as a reference we can then compare all other ions to it. An example will serve to illustrate the calculation. For dilute HCl solution, $\Delta H_f = -40.02$ kcal/mole. But this is composed of the ΔH_f for each ion, and if we set $\Delta H_f(H^+) = 0$, then

$$\Delta H_f(\text{HCl}, aq) = \Delta H_f(\text{H}^+, aq) + \Delta H_f(\text{Cl}^-, aq)$$

$$-40.02 = 0 + \Delta F_f(\text{Cl}^-, aq)$$

Thus

$$\Delta H_f (Cl^-, aq) = -40.02 \text{ kcal/mole}$$

This value, -40.02 kcal/mole for the chloride ion, has no absolute meaning. It is only a relative value, using the hydrogen ion as a point of reference.

It is then possible to take data for dilute solutions of many ionic compounds and compile a list of enthalpies for individual ions. Examples of such data are given in Table 3-2 and many more are included in the standard thermodynamic tables mentioned earlier.

TABLE 3-2. Enthalpies of Formation of Ions in Infinitely Dilute Solution at 25°C, kcal/mole*

Cation	ΔH_f	Anion	ΔH_f
H^+	0.00	OH^-	-54.96
Na^+	-57.28	F^-	-78.66
K^+	-60.04	Cl^-	-40.02
NH_4^+	-31.74	Br^-	-28.90
Mg^{2+}	-110.41	I^-	-13.37
Zn^{2+}	-36.44	S^{2-}	$+10.0$
Cu^{2+}	$+15.39$	SO_4^{2-}	-216.90
Ag^+	$+25.31$	NO_3^-	-49.37
Fe^{2+}	-21.0	CO_3^{2-}	-161.63
Fe^{3+}	-11.4	$C_2H_3O_2^-$	-116.84

*N.B.S. Circular 500.

Example. Calculate ΔH for the reaction:

$$Ag^+NO_3^- (aq) + Na^+Cl^- (aq) \longrightarrow AgCl (s) + Na^+NO_3^- (aq)$$

Here AgCl is a solid and must be considered as such. The NO_3^- and Na^+ ions are not directly involved in the reaction and therefore may be omitted.

$$\Delta H = \Delta H_f (AgCl) - \Delta H_f (Ag^+) - \Delta H_f (Cl^-)$$
$$= -30.36 \quad - 25.31 \quad - (-40.02)$$
$$= -15.65 \text{ kcal}$$

The enthalpies given in Table 3-2 and in the standard compilations are for infinitely dilute solutions, but it is a good approximation to use such "infinite dilution" data for most reactions at concentrations below $1M$. For precise calculations data are available for some compounds giving ΔH_f as a function of concentration.[1]

3-5. Variation of ΔH with Temperature

The discussion so far has been confined to enthalpy changes close to room temperature and primarily to the single temperature of 298°K. Many reactions are studied at other temperatures, and it is therefore of interest to examine the effect of temperature on enthalpy change. The most striking conclusions from data on enthalpy change as a function of temperature is that for most reactions ΔH is nearly independent of temperature. Even over a temperature range of several thousand degrees ΔH does not change by more than a few percent. Thus, for many purposes the effect of temperature on reaction enthalpy can be ignored.

To see why this should be the case we can employ the conservation principle, which lies at the heart of the energy concept. The enthalpy change for a reaction at one temperature (T_1) must differ from the enthalpy change at another temperature (T_2) only by the net amount of thermal energy required to take all reactants from T_1 to T_2 and the products from T_2 back to T_1. Thus, in order to calculate ΔH for the formation of $H_2O(g)$ from its elements at 2000°K, it is necessary to know ΔH for the reaction at some other temperature, e.g., 298°K, plus the following data:[4]

$$H_2(g, 298°) \rightarrow H_2(g, 2000°) \qquad \Delta H° = 12.65 \text{ kcal}$$
$$O_2(g, 298°) \rightarrow O_2(g, 2000°) \qquad \Delta H° = 14.15 \text{ kcal}$$
$$H_2O(g, 298°) \rightarrow H_2O(g, 2000°) \qquad \Delta H° = 17.37 \text{ kcal}$$

[4] "J.A.N.A.F. Thermochemical Tables," The Dow Chemical Co., Midland, Mich., 1961.

Combining these algebraically with

$$H_2(g) + \tfrac{1}{2}O_2(g) \longrightarrow H_2O(g) \qquad \Delta H°_{298°} = -57.80 \text{ kcal}$$

gives

$$H_2(g) + \tfrac{1}{2}O_2(g) \longrightarrow H_2O(g) \qquad \Delta H°_{2000°} = -60.15 \text{ kcal}$$

These results are shown to good advantage in Fig. 3-2. Even over a temperature range of nearly 2000°C the change in ΔH is quite small. The diagram shows that a considerable quantity of energy is needed to raise the temperature of the

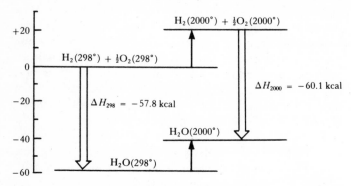

Fig. 3–2.   Enthalpy diagram for the system $H_2(g) + \tfrac{1}{2}O_2(g) \longrightarrow H_2O$ at 298°K and 2000°K, 1 atm in each case.

reactants to 2000°C, but almost the same amount of energy is needed to raise the temperature of the product. This is not particularly surprising when we stop to reflect that the system $(H_2 + \tfrac{1}{2}O_2)$ contains exactly the same number of atoms and the same mass as the system H_2O. There is a major difference in the arrangement of nuclei and electrons in the two systems but this does not significantly affect the energy required simply to change the temperature of the system.

The calculation of the energy change of a substance associated with temperature change is based on the **molar heat**

capacity of that substance. Molar heat capacity is defined as the thermal energy required to raise the temperature of one mole of a substance by 1°C, and for constant pressure processes it is denoted by C_p. In differential notation[5]

$$C_p = q_p/dT \qquad (3\text{-}1)$$

But $q_p = dH$ and therefore

$$C_p = dH/dT \qquad (3\text{-}2)$$

or

$$dH = C_p dT$$

Thus for a change in temperature from T_1 to T_2

$$\Delta H = \int_{T_1}^{T_2} C_p dT \qquad (3\text{-}3)$$

For small temperature ranges C_p is nearly constant and Eq. (3-3) becomes simply $\Delta H = C_p \Delta T$. For calculations over wide temperature ranges, empirical equations are available for many substances which give C_p as a function of temperature and which make possible the integration of Eq. (3-3).

3-6. Summary

In this chapter we have examined in some detail the arithmetic associated with enthalpy calculations. We have considered the problem of reference states in energy calculations, and have found it necessary to introduce two important conventions for assigning energy reference states. These may have raised questions in the mind of the reader as to the justification for such arbitrary procedures. The simple fact is that there is no other choice. We do not know absolute energies with sufficient precision so that they have any chemical meaning. We can, however, discuss in a meaningful way

---

[5] A lower case q is used to indicate an infinitesimal quantity of heat, while Q is used to indicate a finite quantity of heat transferred.

the changes in energy associated with specific chemical changes. It is to facilitate the calculation of energy changes that the arbitrary reference states have been introduced.

In this and the previous chapter we have laid the groundwork for calculations of the energy and enthalpy changes associated with several types of chemical reactions. Chemists are not, in general, particularly interested in energy values alone, but rather in the utilization of energy data for the interpretation of chemical behavior. In the next chapter we shall proceed, therefore, to apply our knowledge to more detailed investigations of some selected chemical systems.

chapter four

ENTHALPY AND STRUCTURE

THE DISCUSSION of enthalpy changes which accompany chemical changes has led to the proposal that each compound can be assigned a standard enthalpy of formation. In many cases this enthalpy of formation can be obtained by direct calorimetric determination of the thermal energy produced when a compound is formed from its elements. For those compounds whose formation reactions are difficult to carry out in a calorimeter indirect calculations are usually possible. By one route or another ΔH_f values have been obtained for large numbers of chemical compounds. We now wish to find out whether these values exhibit any patterns and whether structural interpretations can be assigned to the relative magnitude of the ΔH_f values. We would like to be able to explain why some formation reactions are more favorable energetically than others. (By "energetically" is meant that the reaction results in a state of lower energy for the system.)

We shall begin with the formation of ionic compounds, such as the alkali metal halides. Data for the enthalpies of formation of the 20 alkali metal halides are collected and shown graphically in Fig. 4-1. Although some regular trends in the values are apparent, there is also a puzzling variation exhibited. Enthalpies for the formation of the alkali metal fluorides become less negative with increasing atomic number of the alkali metal, whereas for the chlorides, bromides

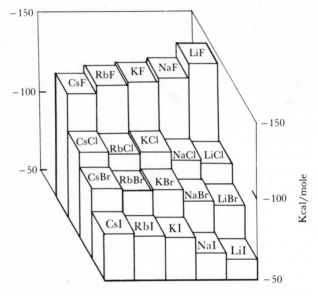

Fig. 4-1. Standard enthalpies of formation for the alkali metal halides, 25°C and 1 atm. (N.B.S. Circular 500.)

and iodides the trend is in the opposite direction. It appears that no single factor can account for the observed variations in ΔH_f.

4-1. Crystal Enthalpies; Born-Haber Cycle

To analyze the enthalpy of formation data a most helpful procedure is to imagine the over-all formation reaction as a series of steps so chosen that they form a thermochemical cycle. This is possible because of the arithmetic properties of enthalpy which were discussed in the previous chapter. For ionic crystals such as the alkali metal halides the energy cycle shown in Fig. 4-2, known as the **Born-Haber cycle**, is particularly useful. (This diagram is referred to as a cycle because if the sign and direction of the arrow for ΔH_f are reversed, the series of steps constitutes a closed loop. Beginning at any point on the diagram and adding the successive enthalpy changes with the correct sign for each, the sum of the ΔH terms for a complete cycle is zero.) The direct formation of the solid compound is indicated in the diagram by the heavy arrow and the corresponding enthalpy change, ΔH_f, is usually easy to obtain experimentally. The alternate clockwise path involves (1) sublimation of the solid metal to gaseous metal atoms (ΔH_S); (2) one half the enthalpy change for dissociation of the halogen molecule ($\frac{1}{2}\Delta H_D$); (3) the ionization potential (I.P.) of gaseous metal atoms to give gaseous metal ions; (4) the electron affinity (E.A.) of the halogen, representing the gain of an electron by a halogen atom to give the gaseous halide ion; and (5) the enthalpy of formation of the crystal from the gaseous ions, which is called the lattice enthalpy (ΔH_L). The two pathways may be expressed by Eq. (4-1).

$$\Delta H_f = \Delta H_S + \tfrac{1}{2}\Delta H_D + \text{I.P.} + \text{E.A.} + \Delta H_L \qquad (4\text{-}1)$$

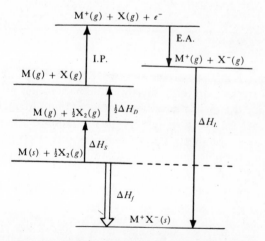

Fig. 4–2. Enthalpy diagram for the formation of alkali metal halides (Born-Haber cycle).

With this equation, any one of the energy terms can be calculated if all the others are known. Historically, the Born-Haber cycle was first used to calculate electron affinities of the halogens. Actually, both electron affinities (E.A.) and lattice enthalpies (ΔH_L) are difficult to measure experimentally, but theoretical lattice enthalpies can be calculated for many ionic crystals.[1]

We can now return to the question, "What factors affect the pattern of formation enthalpies for the alkali metal halides, as shown in Fig. 4-1?" To answer this we need values for the individual terms in Eq. (4-1). Table 4-1 lists some values for four of the compounds in the set: two fluoride

TABLE 4-1. Born-Haber Enthalpy Data for Alkali Metal Halides, kcal/mole at 25°C*

	ΔH_S + I.P.	$\frac{1}{2}\Delta H_D$ + E.A.	ΔH_L	ΔH_f
LiF	+162.9	−79.5	−229.7	−146.3
CsF	+110.1	−79.5	−157.5	−126.9
LiI	+162.9	−50.2	−177.5	− 64.8
CsI	+110.1	−50.2	−140.4	− 80.5

*N.B.S. Circular 500.

compounds at one extreme and two iodide compounds at the other extreme. In the table the sublimation and ionization terms for the metals have been combined into a single term (ΔH_S + I.P.) which represents the formation of the gaseous metal ions. Similarly the dissociation and electron affinity terms for the halogens have been combined into a single term ($\frac{1}{2}\Delta H_D$ + E.A.).

Looking first at the iodides, there is a large drop from

[1] For a further discussion see: L. Pauling, "The Nature of the Chemical Bond," Third Edition, Cornell University Press, Ithaca, New York, 1960; and M. A. Paul, "Principles of Chemical Thermodynamics," McGraw-Hill, New York, 1951.

lithium to cesium iodides in the energy absorbed to form the metal ion (53 kcal). There is simultaneously a decrease of only 37 kcal for the lattice enthalpy, which is a considerably smaller decrease than 53 kcal. The enthalpy term for the formation of the anion remains constant; therefore it is the relative changes indicated in the first and third columns of Table 4-1 which control the change in formation enthalpy. The net result is an increasingly negative enthalpy of formation from lithium to cesium iodide. The same type of reasoning applies (with minor variations) to the bromides and chlorides.

In the case of the fluorides, the variation of $(\Delta H_S + \text{I.P.})$ from lithium to cesium fluoride is the same as for the iodides (53 kcal), but the change in lattice enthalpy (72 kcal) is much greater. The net result, therefore, is a less negative formation enthalpy from lithium to cesium fluoride. The large variation in lattice enthalpies for the fluorides is presumably because the small fluoride ion results in a short distance between positive and negative ion (Table 4-2).

TABLE 4-2. Ionic (Crystal) Radii in Angstroms*

Ion	Radius	Ion	Radius
Li^+	0.60	F^-	1.36
Na^+	0.95	Cl^-	1.81
K^+	1.33	Br^-	1.95
Rb^+	1.48	I^-	2.16
Cs^+	1.69		

*Pauling, *op. cit.*, p. 514.

Variations in the metal ion radius will have a greater relative effect on the interatomic distance than will be the case for the other halide ions, which are all larger than the fluoride ion.

The general trend of more negative formation enthalpies from iodides to fluorides is a reflection both of the increasing electron affinity of the halogens and of the greater lattice enthalpy which is due to the decreasing interionic distance. Thus it is possible to explain the trends within this series of formation energies on the basis of a simple model, and what appears to be a quite anomalous behavior is readily explained when the over-all energy change is considered as made up of several parts.

Still another feature of the reaction of a metal and a halogen is revealed by analysis of the step-wise energy changes. The formation of a metal halide can be imagined to consist first of the formation of gaseous atoms, then the formation of the gaseous ions, and finally the combination of the ions to form a crystal lattice. For sodium chloride the three steps are as follows:

(a) $Na(s) + \frac{1}{2}Cl_2(g) \rightarrow Na(g) + Cl(g)$ $\qquad \Delta H = +55.0 \text{ kcal}$

(b) $Na(g) + Cl(g) \rightarrow Na^+(g) + Cl^-(g)$ $\qquad \Delta H = +32.7 \text{ kcal}$

(c) $Na^+(g) + Cl^-(g) \rightarrow NaCl(s)$ $\qquad \Delta H = -185.9 \text{ kcal}$

The first two steps are endothermic with $\Delta H > 0$. The third step is the one that is exothermic. A common explanation for the formation of metal halide compounds states that the atoms have a tendency to form stable outer shells of eight electrons (or two electrons in the case of Li^+). However, the energy analysis makes it evident that an explanation of the reaction of sodium and chlorine cannot be based on some assumed stability of "filled" electron shells, since the formation of ions results in a state of higher energy for the system. The over-all formation reaction proceeds as it does because of the low energy of the ions when assembled in a crystal lattice to form a solid compound. The reader may wish to verify for himself (by consulting one of the compilations of thermodynamic data) whether step (b) is endothermic for all 20 of the alkali halides shown in Fig. 4-1.

4-2. Covalent Bond Energies

In Sec. 4-1 we were concerned with the formation of ionic compounds, in which the "bonding" forces were assumed to be the electrostatic attractions between individual ions to form an extended crystal lattice. For covalent compounds, the bonding forces are assumed to arise because of pairs of electrons that are simultaneously attracted by two nuclei and that thereby hold a molecule together as a single unit. In order to calculate the covalent bond energy, an energy cycle can be used in which the gaseous atoms are first formed, and these then react to form a covalent molecule.

A suitable cycle is shown diagrammatically for the formation of water in Fig. 4-3. The enthalpy required to dissociate molecular hydrogen is 104.2 kcal/mole, while one-half the enthalpy to dissociate molecular oxygen is 59.2 kcal/mole. The enthalpy of formation, ΔH_f, for water is -58.0 kcal/mole. Combining these as shown in the diagram gives -221.4 kcal for the total enthalpy of bond formation from

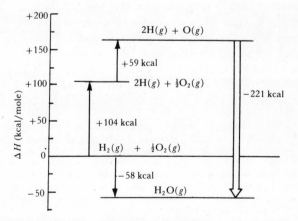

Fig. 4-3. Enthalpy diagram for the system $H_2(g) + \frac{1}{2}O_2(g) \longrightarrow H_2O(g)$, 25°C and 1 atm.

the gaseous atoms. Since two identical H—O bonds are involved, the enthalpy of formation for the H—O bond in water is -110.7 kcal/mole at 25°C.[2]

In a similar manner it is possible to calculate the formation enthalpies for many different types of bonds. For the C—H bond in methane, the appropriate thermochemical equations are as follows.

$$C(\text{graphite}) + 2H_2(g) \rightarrow CH_4(g) \quad \Delta H_{298} = -17.9 \text{ kcal}$$
$$C(\text{graphite}) \rightarrow C(g) \quad \Delta H_{298} = +170.9 \text{ kcal}$$
$$2H_2(g) \rightarrow 4H(g) \quad \Delta H_{298} = +208.4 \text{ kcal}$$

Reversing the last two equations and adding the three equations together gives

$$C(g) + 4H(g) \rightarrow CH_4(g) \quad \Delta H_{298} = -397.2 \text{ kcal}$$

The enthalpy of formation of the C—H bond from gaseous atoms is taken to be one-fourth of this, or -99.3 kcal.

It is of interest to note that all bond enthalpy determinations for carbon compounds must utilize the enthalpy of sublimation of carbon (graphite to gas) in the calculations. This enthalpy has proved to be notoriously difficult to obtain and its magnitude has been a controversial topic for many years.[3] Enthalpies of sublimation have been reported which range from 124 to 176 kcal/mole of carbon. Only recently does the major controversy seem to have been resolved. The most recent value is 170.9 kcal/mole,[4] slightly lower than the

----

[2] It is a common practice among chemists to assign positive values to bond enthalpies, so that these represent the energies which must be added to a system in order to break apart the bonds. We prefer, however, to use the negative numbers, corresponding to the formation reactions, so as to emphasize that a system which contains atoms bonded together is at a lower energy than a system of separated atoms. A bond energy is not an energy that a compound possesses: it is an energy a compound *does not* possess when compared with the gaseous atoms.

[3] (a) Pauling, *op. cit.*, p. 86; (b) T. L. Cottrell, "The Strengths of Chemical Bonds," Second Edition, Butterworths, London, 1958, pp. 155 ff.

[4] "J.A.N.A.F. Thermochemical Tables," The Dow Chemical Co., Midland, Michigan, 1961.

N.B.S. Circular 500 value of 171.7 kcal/mole. There have been similar controversies over the enthalpies of atomization of several other elements. Most notable of these is nitrogen. The enthalpy of formation of $N(g)$ (i.e., one-half the enthalpy of dissociation of N_2) was listed in N.B.S. Circular 500 as 85.6 kcal/mole, whereas the most recent value is 113.0 kcal/mole.[4]

It should be realized that the value -99.3 kcal/mole for the C—H bond enthalpy is not the same as the enthalpy for each step in the addition of successive hydrogen atoms to a carbon atom to form methane. The stepwise enthalpies—although not accurately known—are approximately -80, -124, -88, and -101 kcal/mole,[5] but the average value for the four steps is close to -99 kcal.

It is reasonable to expect that on the average the enthalpy of a C—H bond will be essentially the same in any compound containing C—H bonds; on the other hand, it is also to be expected that there will be at least minor differences depending upon the adjacent atoms and bonds. In practice, "average" or "best fit" values for bond enthalpies can be calculated. Although these may not correspond exactly to any one compound, they fit most compounds within about 2%. Some average bond enthalpies are given in Table 4-3.[6]

These values can be used to calculate the approximate total bond enthalpy of any compound for which individual bond enthalpies are available. For example, the total bond enthalpy of ethyl alcohol, C_2H_5OH, is approximately:

$$
\begin{aligned}
5 \times \text{C—H} &= -495 \\
1 \times \text{C—C} &= -\ 83 \\
1 \times \text{C—O} &= -\ 85 \\
1 \times \text{H—O} &= \underline{-111} \\
&\ \ -774 \text{ kcal/mole}
\end{aligned}
$$

[5] Cottrell, *op. cit.*, p. 270.
[6] For an excellent recent discussion of bond energies and an extensive compilation of available data, the reader is referred to Cottrell.

TABLE 4-3. Bond Enthalpies, kcal/mole at 25°C and 1 atm*

Bond	Bond Enthalpy	Bond	Bond Enthalpy
Cl—Cl	− 58	C—Cl	− 81
N—H	− 93	C—C	− 83
H—Cl	−103	C—O	− 85
H—H	−104	C—H	− 99
H—O	−111	C≡C	−146
O÷O	−118†	C≡O	−177
N≡N	−226‡	C≡C	−200

*Cottrell, *op. cit.*
†Dissociation of O_2.
‡Dissociation of N_2.

Calculations from enthalpy of formation data give a total bond enthalpy of −771 kcal for $C_2H_5OH(g)$, which is in excellent agreement with the above value.

Bond enthalpies can also be used quite effectively to estimate the enthalpy changes in chemical reactions. For example, in the reaction

$$C_2H_6(g) + Cl_2(g) \rightarrow C_2H_5Cl(g) + HCl(g)$$

the only bond changes are the disruption of one C—H bond and a Cl—Cl bond, and the formation of a C—Cl and an H—Cl bond. Using data in Table 4-3, gives $\Delta H = -27$ kcal.

4-3. Solubility of Ionic Crystals

As another application of an energy cycle, let us consider the process of dissolving a crystalline ionic solid (MX) in water. This may occur directly, or may be thought of as consisting of two steps (Fig. 4-4): (1) sublimation of the solid to give free gaseous ions, for which ΔH is the negative of the lattice enthalpy $(-\Delta H_L)$, and (2) hydration of these gaseous ions to give the hydrated ions in solution (ΔH_{hyd}). The reaction, of course, does not normally occur by this two-step path, but energetically must be equivalent to such a path.

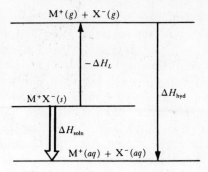

Fig. 4-4. Enthalpy diagram for the dissolving of an ionic crystal.

Hydration enthalpies (ΔH_{hyd}) are difficult to measure, but the enthalpy cycle provides a way to calculate them from lattice and solution enthalpies.

$$\Delta H_{hyd} = \Delta H_{soln} + \Delta H_L \qquad (4\text{-}2)$$

A further usefulness of such an enthalpy cycle is that it enables us to analyze the factors which contribute to the enthalpy of solution. Table 4-4 lists data for several chloride salts. In the case of lithium chloride, the hydration enthalpy is larger (more negative) than the lattice enthalpy. In other words, the attraction of the ions for water molecules is greater than the attraction of the ions for each other within

TABLE 4-4. Lattice, Hydration, and Solution Enthalpies, kcal/o le, 25°C and 1 atm*

Compound	ΔH_L (kcal/mole)	ΔH_{hyd} (kcal/mole)	ΔH_{soln} (kcal/mole)	Solubility (moles/liter)
LiCl	−202.3	−211.2	− 8.9	19.2
NaCl	−185.9	−185.0	+ .9	6.2
KCl	−169.0	−164.9	+ 4.1	4.8
AgCl	−217.4	−201.7	+15.7	1.3×10^{-5}

*N.B.S. Circular 500.

the crystal lattice. The net result is a lower enthalpy for the solution than for the separated solute and solvent. This is consistent with the observation that lithium chloride is readily soluble in water. For sodium chloride, the lattice and hydration enthalpies are nearly equal, the crystal being slightly lower in enthalpy than the solution. Sodium chloride is in fact less soluble than lithium chloride. Notice that the lattice enthalpy for NaCl is smaller in magnitude than for LiCl, but that there is even more difference in hydration enthalpies. It is this increased difference in hydration enthalpies which must account for the differing values of ΔH_{soln}. Notice also, however, that ΔH_{soln} represents only a small net difference between two large energy quantities.

Silver chloride, on the other hand, has a large hydration enthalpy (nearly as large as lithium chloride), but it also has an even larger lattice enthalpy. The net result is an enthalpy balance strongly in favor of the crystal, a conclusion which agrees at least qualitatively with the extremely low solubility of silver chloride in water. The large lattice enthalpy of silver chloride can be attributed to the polarizability of the silver ion, resulting in partial covalent bonding in addition to the simple electrostatic interaction of the ions.

4-4. Interpretation of Electrode Reactions

Reactions such as the one described by

$$Zn(s) + Cu^{2+}(aq) \rightarrow Zn^{2+}(aq) + Cu(s) \qquad \Delta H = -51.82 \text{ kcal}$$

provide systems for which an energy analysis can illuminate some aspects of the nature of the reaction. The reaction of zinc and copper(II) ion is often referred to as a change which proceeds because of the tendency of zinc to transfer electrons to copper ions. Such an electron transfer mechanism suggests that we might divide the over-all reaction into several steps as follows.

$$Zn(s) \rightarrow Zn(g) \qquad \Delta H = 31.2 \text{ kcal}$$
$$Zn(g) \rightarrow Zn^{2+} \qquad \Delta H = 633.7 \text{ kcal}$$
$$Zn^{2+}(g) \rightarrow Zn^{2+}(aq) \qquad \Delta H = -701.3 \text{ kcal}$$

$$Cu(s) \rightarrow Cu(g) \qquad \Delta H = 81.5 \text{ kcal}$$
$$Cu(g) \rightarrow Cu^{2+}(g) \qquad \Delta H = 648.6 \text{ kcal}$$
$$Cu^{2+}(g) \rightarrow Cu^{2+}(aq) \qquad \Delta H = -714.7 \text{ kcal}$$

The relationship among these steps can be seen in Fig. 4-5a. In this diagram the system consisting of the separate gaseous ions plus two electrons has been chosen as the reference state at the top of the diagram. Two alternate reaction paths are indicated by separate vertical lines. In the left-hand path Zn^{2+} acquires the two electrons and Cu^{2+} becomes hydrated. By the right-hand path Cu^{2+} acquires two electrons and Zn^{2+} becomes hydrated. The enthalpy change for the complete reaction is indicated on the diagram by the difference in position of the two lowest horizontal lines. From gaseous ions to gaseous metal atoms plus hydrated ions the energy changes are virtually identical for the alternate paths in the diagram. Therefore, electron transfer between atoms does not seem to be the crucial aspect determining the direction of the over-all reaction. Comparison of the sublimation energies for the two metals indicates a difference in energy (50.3 kcal) almost identical to the energy change associated with the over-all reaction.

It seems reasonable to conclude that for zinc metal and copper(II) ions a reaction proceeds because of differences between solid zinc and solid copper. For solid copper to be at a lower energy than solid zinc suggests that electrons pack more tightly around copper nuclei than around zinc nuclei. The molar volumes of these two metals, 9.16 ml/mole for Zn and 7.13 ml/mole for Cu, are consistent with such an interpretation of the enthalpy changes.

Differences in sublimation energy are not crucial to the interpretation of all electrode reactions, however. In Fig.

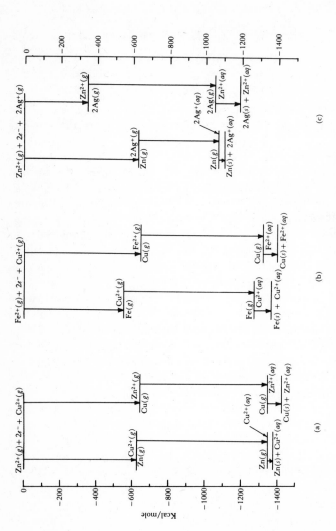

Fig. 4-5.   Enthalpy changes for some electrode reactions at 25°C.

4-5b data are presented for the reaction described by

$$Fe(s) + Cu^{2+}(aq) \rightarrow Fe^{2+}(aq) + Cu(s) \qquad \Delta H = -36.4 \, kcal$$

Here the formation of hydrated iron(II) ions provides a lower energy than does the formation of hydrated copper(II) ions. Sublimation energies, on the other hand, actually favor solid iron rather than solid copper.[7]

4-5. Summary

In this chapter enthalpy calculations have been used in the investigation of some of the factors involved in chemical change. We have looked at several major types of reactions: the formation of ionic crystals from pure elements, the formation of covalently bonded compounds from the elements, the dissolving of ionic crystals to produce aqueous solutions, and reactions involving metal electrodes.

The process of ionic crystal formation from the elements was analyzed by breaking the process up into a number of terms. Although the formation reaction is not carried out experimentally in such a stepwise manner, the two paths are equivalent in energy, and it is this equivalence which makes it possible to investigate the system in detail. From the relative magnitudes of the several terms, we were able to show which ones account for the major differences in experimental formation enthalpies within a group of similar compounds. Such an investigation considerably enhances knowledge of chemical reactivity.

In a somewhat analogous manner the enthalpy of formation of a covalent compound was imagined to consist of several steps, and a calculation was made for that step which describes the bond formation alone. Information on bond energies finds wide application in modern chemistry.

[7] For some further interesting interpretations of enthalpy changes see: C. R. Allen and P. G. Wright, *Nature*, **199,** 344 (1963).

It is important to realize that this discussion of bond energies and molecular structure is not essential to the study of thermodynamics. Classical thermodynamics was in fact developed before chemists had any very precise knowledge of bonds and molecular structure. The energy and enthalpy changes which accompany chemical reactions are calculated directly from experiments, without any assumptions about the arrangement of electrons and nuclei within the system. On the other hand, we often wish to interpret thermodynamic properties in relation to structural changes involving individual atoms and molecules.

Although enthalpy data are important and widely used, the next chapter will show that another quantity is ultimately of crucial significance in describing the feasibility of chemical change. Nevertheless, the techniques developed here and in the preceding chapter for computing energy changes and for analyzing chemical systems can be applied equally well to other energy quantities.

chapter five

THE DIRECTION
OF CHANGE

A QUESTION of primary interest to chemists is, "Will these substances react when brought together?" A reaction that proceeds by itself is said to be **spontaneous**. No implication is intended, however, as to how rapidly the reaction will proceed, and therefore it is sometimes better to describe a reaction that may proceed by itself as a *feasible reaction*. Thus, for example, a mixture of hydrogen and oxygen gases at room temperature may show no evidence of reaction, but addition of a small amount of a catalyst shows that the reaction is indeed feasible! Both terms, spontaneous and feasible, will be used in subsequent discussions of the question of whether substances can react.

5-1. Energy Transfer and Chemical Change

For many years chemists believed that data on the heats of reactions provided an answer to the question of reaction feasibility. The idea developed that a reaction is feasible only if heat is evolved. According to this reasoning, a reaction at constant pressure is feasible only if ΔH is negative. On the other hand, a system that gains energy during a change requires the cooperation of the environment which supplies the energy, and so the change cannot proceed spontaneously.

There are many examples of systems in which the observed change is accompanied by an enthalpy decrease (see, for example, the data in Table 3-1). Experience with certain other chemical systems, however, is disconcerting. When a solution of Na_2CO_3 is mixed with a solution of $CaCl_2$ in an insulated container, a precipitate forms and the system in its final state is at a lower temperature than in its initial state. The reaction is described by

$$Na_2CO_3(aq) + CaCl_2(aq) \rightarrow CaCO_3(s) + 2NaCl(aq)$$

If equal volumes of 1 M solutions are mixed, the temperature change, ΔT, is found to be approximately $-1.4°C$. In other words, for this system to change at constant temperature, energy is absorbed and not evolved.

A further puzzle is encountered when one examines the enthalpy changes for precipitation of the series of alkaline earth carbonates. Since these compounds are all quite similar chemically, we might expect the ΔH values to be similar; however, as shown in Table 5-1, there is a considerable

TABLE 5-1. Enthalpy Changes for Precipitation of Alkaline Earth Carbonates*

Reaction	$\Delta H°_{298}$ (kcal)
$Mg^{2+}(aq) + CO_3^{2-}(aq) \rightarrow MgCO_3(s)$	+6.
$Ca^{2+}(aq) + CO_3^{2-}(aq) \rightarrow CaCO_3(s)$	+2.9
$Sr^{2+}(aq) + CO_3^{2-}(aq) \rightarrow SrCO_3(s)$	+0.8
$Ba^{2+}(aq) + CO_3^{2-}(aq) \rightarrow BaCO_3(s)$	−1.0

*N.B.S. Circular 500.

variation in magnitude. Only one compound, $BaCO_3$, has a negative ΔH, yet all four are found to precipitate readily from aqueous solution.

Consider two other cases of positive energy change. When water or any other liquid vaporizes at a constant temperature it absorbs energy.

$$H_2O(l) \quad \rightarrow \quad H_2O(g) \qquad \Delta H_{373} = +9.72 \, \text{kcal}$$

Vaporization is a process that can go on quite readily to give a final state of higher energy than the initial state. Carbon reacts readily with steam at 1000°K, as described by the equation

$$C(s) + H_2O(g) \rightarrow CO(g) + H_2(g) \qquad \Delta H_{1000} = +32.42 \, \text{kcal}$$

but thermal energy must be added to keep the temperature constant as the reaction proceeds. These examples make clear that whatever may be the details of the energy change accompanying a chemical change, the evolution of thermal energy does not give a completely adequate picture of the reaction.

There is a still further difficulty associated with the use of energy data as a criterion for change. Energy has been defined as something that is conserved. This means that whenever energy is transferred out of a system, an identical quantity of energy is absorbed by the surroundings. Thus, at constant pressure, a decrease in the enthalpy of a system implies an equal increase in the enthalpy of the surroundings. In symbolic form

$$\Delta H_{\text{sys}} = -\Delta H_{\text{sur}} = Q_p \qquad (5\text{-}1)$$

For any form of energy transfer a similar relation must exist. Whatever the energy change associated with the system, it is, by definition, precisely mirrored by an energy change in the surroundings. Indeed, the first law of thermodynamics refers to exactly the same point by stressing that internal energy can change only as a consequence of an energy transfer between a system and its surroundings.

But if energy transfer always produces equal and opposite effects in the system and surroundings, we are forced to conclude that energy is thereby an unlikely criterion for the ability of a system to change. A reason established for the energy change of the system in one direction must be matched by some reason for the surroundings to change in energy in the opposite way. By this reasoning it appears that no conservative property can be used as a criterion for the possibility of change.

5-2. Probability and Change

If a conservative property such as energy cannot be a criterion for the possibility of change, then we must look for some aspect of change which is nonconservative. One such nonconservative property is the degree of order which systems possess. This is exhibited, for example, by a deck of cards which, if sorted and arranged in some chosen order of low probability, always gets a less orderly more probable arrangement when shuffled. We simply do not anticipate that shuffling will lead to any more orderly arrangement. Similarly, a message written out in a carefully chosen and hence orderly form always becomes more garbled and disorderly—or at least never more orderly—when transmitted through a system that requires rewriting the message. For each of these systems the order is observed to decrease without any corresponding change in the surroundings. Hence a decrease in order can be nonconservative.

It would appear from these and other observations that the world must be continually increasing in the degree of disorder or randomness. It is true that we may single out systems for study which change in a direction of increased order, but this is always accompanied by a change toward even greater disorder of the surroundings. Order can be produced in a system only at the expense of order in the surroundings and always with a net loss in the transaction. The change in total order is thus a one-way change.

A simple system can be used to exhibit more quantitatively the one-way aspect of change. Let us consider the expansion of 1 mole of gas from a volume, V, to twice the volume, $2V$, by allowing it to expand into a vacuum. What is the probability that this will occur? Conversely, what is the probability that it will not occur?

Suppose there is one molecule in a box. Let us further suppose that we can observe whether the molecule is in one end or the other end of the box. What is the probability that at any instant it will be in the left end of the box? If this molecule can move freely throughout the box, we would expect to find it in the left end of the box on about one half of the observations we make in a given time. This is the same thing as saying that the probability is $\frac{1}{2}$ that the molecule will be in the left end.

Now suppose there are two molecules, A and B, in the box. We would expect A in the left end about half the time and B in the left end about half the time. It is then reasonable to say that for about one out of four observations we would expect to find both A and B in the left end. Thus the probability of both A and B being in the left end may be obtained by multiplying the probabilities that A and B, considered separately, are in the left end, or $\frac{1}{2} \times \frac{1}{2} = \frac{1}{4}$. For three molecules the probability that all three are together in the left end is $\frac{1}{2} \times \frac{1}{2} \times \frac{1}{2} = (\frac{1}{2})^3$. For n molecules it is $(\frac{1}{2})^n$.

For a mole of molecules the probability that all will be in the left end of the box is $\frac{1}{2}$ with the exponent 6×10^{23}, where 6×10^{23} is Avogadro's number. This is a fantastically small probability. But if the probability of this event occurring is so extremely small, then the probability of the opposite situation is extremely close to 1. In other words, dispersion of the molecules throughout the whole container is highly probable.

Imagine now a container divided in half by a partition, with gas on one side and a vacuum on the other. If the partition is removed, will the gas expand to fill the container uniformly? If there are only a few particles present, the probability that they will become evenly distributed throughout the container is great, yet there is always at least a slight possibility that an uneven distribution will develop. For 10 particles there is about one chance in a thousand that they will not evenly distribute, for 20 particles about one chance in a million. But for a mole of gas, with many, many billions of molecules, the probability of an uneven distribution is vanishingly small, and we may say with confidence that the gas will expand to fill the container.

The point of all this is that high probability is associated with the state for which particles are distributed as randomly as possible, and in chemical systems with very large numbers of particles the "probability push" toward more random arrangements is extremely large. The discussion so far has centered on the relatively simple case of gas expansion. Most chemical changes are considerably more complicated than this, but it is not unreasonable to expect that the same general principle holds. We may conclude, therefore, that a change is feasible if it results in a state of greater randomness.

Let us consider now the formation of a chemical bond. If the bond is formed from isolated atoms, such as the reaction

$$H(g) \quad + \quad Cl(g) \quad \rightarrow \quad HCl(g) \quad \Delta H \quad = \quad -103 \, kcal$$

the net result must be an increased order, or decreased randomness, since the H—Cl bond implies an arrangement of the particles in pairs. The decrease in randomness of the structural units must therefore be accompanied by another change toward greater randomness. This latter change may take one of two forms. At constant pressure and temperature heat will be transferred from the system to the surroundings and the surroundings will increase in random thermal motion. Alternatively, in an adiabatic process ($\Delta H = 0$) the reaction will lead to an increase in temperature and hence increased random thermal motion of the system. In either case, the increase in random thermal motion will have to be more than sufficient to counterbalance the organization produced by the formation of a bond.

As one more example, consider the vaporization of water at constant temperature.

$$H_2O(l) \quad \rightarrow \quad H_2O(g)$$

Probability favors this reaction because in the resulting gas the water molecules are much more randomly distributed than in the relatively compact liquid. The situation is similar to the gas expansion discussed earlier, but more dramatic. Instead of a mere doubling of volume, the vaporization of 1 mole of water at 100°C and 1 atm results in a volume increase of about 1500. But if probability favors this change, what about the change in the surroundings? The increased randomness of the water in the vapor phase is accompanied by a decreased randomness in the surroundings. Above 100°C we know the reaction takes place readily; therefore we conclude that the increased randomness of the water is larger than the decreased randomness of the surroundings. Below 100°C at 1 atm the reaction does not take place readily, so the reverse must be true.

5-3. Reversible and Irreversible Processes

In the previous section probability arguments led to a possible explanation for the direction of certain changes. In a qualitative way the argument seems convincing, yet no way to assign numerical values to this property has been provided. We shall therefore return to a discussion of measured quantities: the heat and work which are transferred between a system and its surroundings during a change in the state of the system.

For a given change in state a definite amount of energy must be transferred, since ΔE is determined only by the initial and final states of the system. However, there are several ways in which this transfer of energy may occur: the energy may be transferred as *heat* because of some temperature difference between system and surroundings, or as *work* because of some difference in motion or potential, or as a combination of the two. This is summarized by the First Law of Thermodynamics, previously given as Eq. (2-2):

$$\Delta E = Q + W \qquad (5\text{-}2)$$

Let us now consider two extreme possibilities for carrying out the change: the process in which the maximum useful work is performed and the process in which no useful work is performed. The simplest type of system for purposes of illustration is a gas which is allowed to expand from a volume V_1 to a larger volume V_2. The expanding gas can transfer work to the surroundings only if it pushes against an external pressure exerted by the surroundings. For example, the expanding gas in the cylinder of an automobile does work by pushing against the piston, which is in turn coupled to the rest of the machinery of the automobile. If there is no opposing pressure the gas expands freely from V_1 to V_2, but transfers no useful work. Expansion without work can be produced by allowing a gas to expand into a vacuum. The probability of a mole of gas doubling its volume was shown to be extremely high—yet if there is no opposing pressure no useful work is accomplished.

Suppose we now carry out the expansion from V_1 to V_2 but with some arbitrarily chosen external pressure. From Eq. (2-3) we know that

$$W = -P_{\text{sur}} \Delta V \qquad (5\text{-}3)$$

where P_{sur} is the opposing pressure exerted on the system by the surroundings. Therefore, as P_{sur} increases there will be a corresponding increase in the amount of useful work performed by the system. But is there a limit to how much useful work can be done? If the pressure of the system is slightly greater than the opposing pressure, the expansion occurs and work is done on the surroundings. However, if the opposing pressure becomes equal to the pressure of the system, there is no net push in either direction; thus no change takes place in the system, and no work is actually performed. If the opposing pressure becomes slightly greater than the pressure of the system, then work is done, but on the system by the surroundings. Thus we are led to the conclusion that the maximum amount of work is approached most closely when the pressure of a system is only infinitesimally greater than the opposing pressure. The process can be made to go in the opposite direction by an infinitesimally small change in the relative pressures, and the change is therefore said to occur by a **reversible process**.

A reversible process is, unfortunately, hypothetical, because it can be approached but never achieved. As system pressure and surrounding pressure approach each other more and more closely, the work transferred becomes greater; but if system and surrounding pressures are equal, no change occurs. Any change which is actually observed, such as the reaction of one mole of a chemical substance, must involve something less than the maximum amount of work and is therefore said to proceed by an **irreversible process**.

Reversible and irreversible processes have been exemplified by the expansion of a gas, but the conclusion reached is a general one. All systems which transfer energy to the surroundings in the form of work do so by operating against some opposing force. The hypothetical reversible process is one that transfers the maximum amount of energy as work; yet all real processes produce something less than the maximum work and are at least partially irreversible. The significance of the reversible process is that it describes an upper limit to the possible work and therefore represents a measure of the *capacity* for doing work which the system possesses. At the other extreme, a system may change by a process in which no work at all is done. This would be the completely irreversible case. No matter what amount of work may be transferred by a given change—from zero to nearly the maximum—the *capacity* of the system to transfer energy as work changes by a fixed amount, which is equal to the reversible work.

The transfer of heat from system to surroundings can occur only if the temperature of the system is higher than that of the surroundings. Once transferred from high to low temperature, the heat cannot by itself make the return transfer, since a given quantity of heat has never been observed to go from a low to a high temperature without some other simultaneous energy transfer. On the other hand, the transfer of work encounters no such difficulty and is observed to proceed in either direction without regard to temperature differences or the need for any other energy transfer.

Once the state of the system has changed by ΔE by an irreversible process, the system and surroundings can no longer *both* be restored to their initial conditions. When the system changes irreversibly, less than the maximum work is done on the surroundings; but in order to restore the system to its initial state, the surroundings must do at least as much work as the reversible work on the system. The surroundings therefore always receive less work than must later be transferred back to the system. The only compensation is that the surroundings receive more heat than must later be transferred back to the system. But the net result of restoring the system to its initial condition is a reduction in the capacity of the surroundings for doing work. Only when the system changes reversibly is there any possibility that the restoration can be made to initial conditions of *both* system and surroundings. An irreversible change thus seems to represent a loss of possibilities for future energy transfer, even though no energy is lost during the change.

In terms of order and disorder we may picture this as follows. In a reversible process any disorder created in the system would be exactly offset by increased order produced in the surroundings. The reversible process would be the case of most effective "coupling" between system and surroundings. If the change were reversed, the system would become more ordered, but only at the expense of the surroundings. The work transferred out of the system in the first step would exactly equal the work transferred out of the surroundings in the return step, if both steps were performed reversibly. For the irreversible case, the "coupling" is not completely effective, and the increased disorder of the system is not completely matched by an increased order of the surroundings. To bring the system after a change in state irreversibly back to its starting condition the increased order of the system will be less than the increase in disorder of the surroundings.

We may summarize this by saying that in the first step the system loses a certain capacity to do work, but actually transfers somewhat less than the maximum amount of work to the surroundings; in the return step the surroundings must do more than this "maximum" amount of work to bring the system back to its initial state and thereby restore the initial capacity for work. There is thus a net expenditure of work and a net increase in disorder of the surroundings.

5-4. Entropy

In order to provide a means for measuring the irreversibility of a given change, we shall introduce a new function called **entropy** for which the symbol S is used. Entropy may be defined as follows: when a system undergoes a change in state at constant temperature, the entropy change for the system equals the heat transfer for a reversible process divided by the absolute temperature.[1]

$$\Delta S_{sys} = Q_{rev}/T \qquad (5\text{-}4)$$

The quantity Q_{rev}/T represents a limiting case for heat transfer. No matter by what process the change actually

[1] For a more rigorous development of these ideas, the reader may consult a physical chemistry text, such as G. M. Barrow, "Physical Chemistry," McGraw-Hill Book Co., New York, 1961.

takes place, there is only one reversible process, and ΔS_{sys} is therefore dependent only upon the initial and final states of the system. On the other hand the entropy change in the surroundings, ΔS_{sur}, is not a function of the change in state of the system, but will vary with the process by which the change takes place. Using Q_{irrev} to denote the heat transfer for any irreversible process, we may define ΔS_{sur} as

$$\Delta S_{sur} = -Q_{irrev}/T \qquad (5\text{-}5)$$

The total entropy change must then be

$$\Delta S_{tot} = \Delta S_{sys} + \Delta S_{sur}$$
$$= \frac{Q_{rev} - Q_{irrev}}{T} \qquad (5\text{-}6)$$

For a fixed energy change, ΔE, it can be argued rather simply that Q_{rev} is less negative than Q_{irrev} for exothermic processes or more positive than Q_{irrev} for endothermic processes. Thus it must always be that

$$\frac{Q_{rev} - Q_{irrev}}{T} > 0$$

and, therefore, from Eq. 5-6 that

$$\Delta S_{tot} > 0 \qquad (5\text{-}7)$$

For a given change in a system, ΔS_{sys} is given by just one numerical quantity, but ΔS_{sur} will differ according to the different processes by which the change is accomplished. In all cases, however, ΔS_{tot} will be positive.

In Sec. 5-2 the concept of order and disorder was introduced, with the suggestion that spontaneous change is always in the direction of more disorder or randomness. We have subsequently examined the aspects of the irreversibility of change and described the function called entropy, which permits the calculation from heat transfer data of the magnitude of the irreversible loss that accompanies all spontaneous changes. The obvious question is whether these two ideas are related. The answer to this question is yes; however, it is beyond the scope of this book to give the mathematical background necessary to demonstrate the equivalence in a satisfactory manner. The calculations are difficult to carry out for all but the simplest systems, but in these cases the results are highly satisfactory.

The postulate called the First Law of Thermodynamics states that a system can change in energy only by a transfer of energy between system and surroundings. From the discussion of entropy so far, it is apparent that entropy is fundamentally different from energy and also that entropy must play a decisive role in the analysis of chemical change. We shall postulate therefore a statement known as the **Second Law of Thermodynamics**. Unfortunately, we cannot state this second law with the same precision and simplicity as the first. No simple statement can convey its full meaning. Nevertheless a few of the more common statements are the following:

"Any system if left to itself at constant energy will change only toward a state of maximum probability."

"The energy of the universe is constant, but the entropy of the universe is increasing."

"It is impossible to construct a machine operating in cycles that will absorb heat from the surroundings and deliver work without producing any other changes in surroundings."

5-5. Free Energy

Two factors hare now been introduced which appear to contribute to the direction of chemical change. There is a tendency for a spontaneous change to be favored by an enthalpy decrease in the system ($\Delta H_{sys} < 0$). There is also a tendency for a spontaneous change to be favored by an increase in the entropy of a system ($\Delta S_{sys} > 0$). For some reactions these two factors are both favorable; in other cases one is favorable and the other is not. For the reaction

$$H(g) \; + \; Cl(g) \; \rightarrow \; HCl(g)$$

the enthalpy change is favorable while the entropy change is unfavorable. For the vaporization of liquid water, the enthalpy change is unfavorable while the entropy change is favorable. Clearly what is needed is some way of relating these two factors. To do so we shall introduce a new function, called the **Gibbs free energy change** or simply **free energy change,** for which the symbol is ΔG.[2] This function is defined in such a way that, at constant pressure and temperature,

$$\Delta G_{sys} = \Delta H_{sys} - T \Delta S_{sys} \qquad (5\text{-}8)$$

The factor T must be included with ΔS in order to convert the entropy term into energy units (see Eq. 5-4). Strictly speaking, ΔG is not an energy because it can be shown that it is not a conservative function. Nevertheless, it has the dimensions of energy and in common usage it is referred to as an energy. (Many physicists and a few chemists now prefer the term "Gibbs function change" in order to avoid completely the implication that ΔG is an energy.) The subscripts are given in Eq. (5-8) to emphasize that this relation refers to the system only. ΔH_{sys} must be mirrored by an equal but opposite ΔH_{sur} (so long as the pressures of system and surroundings are the same), but this is not true of ΔS_{sys} and, therefore, also not true for ΔG_{sys}. It is common practice among chemists, however, to omit these subscripts.

Examination of Eq. (5-8) shows that negative ΔH and positive ΔS values both lead to negative ΔG values. We

---

[2]The International Union of Pure and Applied Chemistry has proposed the symbol G for free energy related to constant pressure and constant temperature processes. This is, in part to honor the distinguished American scientist J. Willard Gibbs. His studies at Yale University in the latter part of the 19th century developed many of the ideas upon which understanding of chemical energy now rests. Most American textbooks and scientific reports have in the past used the symbol F, while Europeans have used G. It is curious to observe some Americans resisting the attempt of an international body to honor an American Scientist.

may therefore summarize the possibilities for change at constant pressure and constant temperature as follows:

$$\Delta G < 0: \text{feasible change}$$
$$\Delta G > 0: \text{unfeasible change}$$
$$(\Delta G = 0: \text{state of equilibrium})$$

In order to gain a greater understanding of the nature of the free energy function, it is useful to examine Eq. (5-8) in further detail. Substitution for ΔH in Eq. (5-8) gives

$$\Delta G = (\Delta E + P\Delta V + V\Delta P) - T\Delta S$$

Eq. (5-8) was defined for constant pressure processes; therefore $V\Delta P = 0$. From Eq. (2-2), $\Delta E = Q + W$ and thus

$$\Delta G = Q + W + P\Delta V - T\Delta S$$

If we now impose the restriction of a reversible process, Eq. (5-4) may be used to substitute for $T\Delta S$ as follows:

$$\Delta G = Q_{\text{rev}} + W_{\text{rev}} + P\Delta V - Q_{\text{rev}}$$
$$= W_{\text{rev}} + P\Delta V \qquad (5\text{-}9)$$

W_{rev} is the total possible work for a reversible process. $P\Delta V$ is the work associated with volume change of the system against a constant pressure, P, and if the system expands, then $P\Delta V$ will be a negative number. Thus the quantity $(W_{\text{rev}} + P\Delta V)$ is the total reversible work *minus* the work of expansion of the system. Using W_{max} to represent this difference, we may write

$$W_{\text{max}} = W_{\text{rev}} - (-P\Delta V)$$
$$= W_{\text{rev}} + P\Delta V \qquad (5\text{-}10)$$

W_{max} is thus the work associated with a reversible process other than the work of expansion against the atmosphere. The significance of this is that work of expansion is not "useful" work. It is present unavoidably for any reaction in an open container under atmospheric pressure—no matter how irreversibly the change takes place—but it cannot be harnessed for any useful purpose.

Substituting Eq. (5-10) into (5-9), gives

$$\Delta G = W_{max} \tag{5-11}$$

Therefore, we arrive at the important conclusion that the free energy change, as defined by Eq. (5-8), represents the maximum capacity of the system to transfer energy as useful work at constant pressure and temperature.

Is it possible to measure free energy changes? A direct measure of maximum work transfer is rarely practical because for any process carried on in the laboratory the work transferred is always at least slightly less than the maximum. For some systems, however, it is possible to measure the *capacity* of the system to do work. This is illustrated most easily with measurements of electric potentials. These can be measured with high precision and thus constitute an important laboratory method of free energy determinations.

5-6. Electric Potentials and Free Energy Change

A system which has a capacity to do work is said to have a potential energy. Thus, an object at a high level in a gravitational field has a capacity to do work that it does not have at a low level. This capacity can be calculated from measurements of the field strength and the height. Similarly, a system which has an electric potential difference has a capacity to do work. A measurement of electric potential difference gives a measure of the maximum work which the system has the capacity to deliver during charge flow.

The voltaic pile made up of alternating copper and zinc plates in salt solution was mentioned in Chapter 1 as an electric energy source. However, a modified version of the pile is more suitable for quantitative studies. A dilute solution of copper sulfate is placed in a beaker, together with a piece of copper metal, and a solution of zinc sulfate of equal concentration is placed in a second beaker, together with a piece of zinc metal. To complete the circuit, a U-shaped tube is filled with a concentrated salt solution and placed so that one of the two ends is in each container. A sketch of the arrangement is given in Fig. 5-1. Such an arrangement of metal plates and solutions is called an **electrochemical cell,** or simply a **cell**.

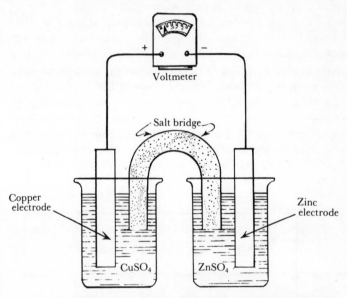

Fig. 5–1. A cell for measuring the electric potential difference between a copper electrode and a zinc electrode.

What is the voltage produced by this cell under conditions of nearly maximum energy output? One way to determine this is to apply an opposing external voltage to the cell (Fig. 5-2) and measure with an ammeter the current which flows through the circuit for various values of the external voltage. Fig. 5-3 is a plot of the data from a typical experiment. It indicates that there is a particular voltage, 1.10

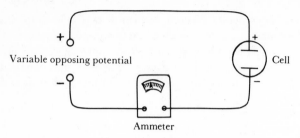

Fig. 5-2.   Circuit for determination of cell potential.

volts, for which no current flows.   Below 1.10 volts current flows in one direction.   When the external voltage becomes greater than 1.10 volts, current flows in the opposite direction.   At exactly 1.10 volts the cell is said to be capable of operating reversibly, and thus 1.10 volts is the maximum possible voltage for the cell itself.   It is true of course that no current is actually flowing and no reaction is taking place, but this represents the maximum *capacity* of the cell for producing electric energy.

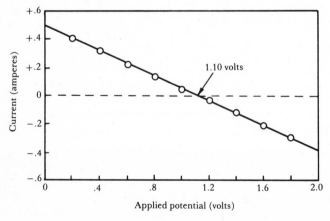

Fig. 5-3.   Current versus applied potential, copper–zinc cell, 25°C.
$CuSO_4$ and $ZnSO_4$ both 1 molar.

The work produced by a cell in the form of electric energy is equal to the potential difference (voltage) multiplied by the total flow of charge (Sec. 1-6). For reaction of one mole of reagent the electric energy is given by

$$W = -nF\mathcal{E} \tag{5-12}$$

where $\mathcal{E}$ is the potential difference in volts, F is the Faraday constant (96,500 coulombs/mole of electrons), and n is the moles of electrons per mole of reagent.

The reaction of one mole of zinc in the above cell involves a total charge flow of 2 moles of electrons. Therefore the maximum electric energy which this cell can transfer as work is

$$W_{max} = -2 \times 96,500 \text{ coulombs} \times 1.10 \text{ volts}$$
$$= -212,000 \text{ joules}$$

Converting to kilocalories (Sec. 1-6) gives

$$W_{max} = -212,000 \text{ joules} \times 0.239 \text{ cal/joule}$$
$$= -50.7 \text{ kcal/mole of Zn consumed}$$

In the previous section, W_{max} was identified as a measure of the free energy change for the system (Eq. 5-11). From this relationship and Eq. (5-12) we see that

$$\Delta G_{sys} = W_{max} = -nF\mathcal{E}_{max} \tag{5-13}$$

This now gives us a straight forward way to measure ΔG, because zero current voltages are comparatively easy to measure. It should be possible therefore to determine ΔG for any reaction that can be arranged as an electrochemical cell.

The chemistry of the zinc-copper cell reaction may now be summarized as follows. The free energy change for the conversion of one mole of zinc and one mole of 1 M copper sulfate solution into copper and 1 M zinc sulfate solution is -50.7 kcal. The corresponding enthalpy change for reaction of zinc with 1 M copper sulfate is found from calorimetric measurements to be -52.1 kcal. The entropy change is, therefore, from Eq. (5-8)

$$\Delta S_{sys} = \frac{\Delta H - \Delta G}{T}$$

$$= \frac{-52.1 - (-50.7)}{298}$$

$$= \frac{1.4}{298} \text{ kcal/deg-mole}$$

If no work is done when the reaction takes place at constant temperature, 52.1 kcal of heat must be transferred to the surroundings. If on the other hand the maximum work is done, then 50.7 kcal will be transferred as work. The remaining 1.4 kcal in this case would be transferred as heat, with the result that the entropy of the system decreases by 1.4/298 kcal/deg-mole. If done reversibly the entropy of the surroundings increases by 1.4/298 kcal/deg-mole and the total entropy change is zero. If done completely irreversibly, the entropy of the system still changes by the same amount, $-1.4/298$ kcal/deg-mole, but the entropy of the surroundings increases by 52.1/298 kcal/deg-mole. The total entropy change for the most irreversible process is thus

$$\Delta S_{tot} = -1.4/298 + 52.1/298 = 50.7/298 \text{ kcal/deg-mole}$$

It should be apparent that a positive ΔS_{tot} for the most irreversible process and a negative ΔG for the reversible process are equivalent measures of the feasibility of a chemical change. In some ways ΔS_{tot} is a better function to use because it focuses attention on what happens in both the system and the surroundings. If a change actually occurs, it does so only because the combined entropy change of the system and surroundings is favorable. The disadvantage, however, of using ΔS_{tot} for computations is that the particular process must be specified. By using ΔG, we focus attention on the system only and use a function which is a measure of the maximum capacity for change under some most favorable set of conditions. Because ΔG is the same regardless of the actual process by which the state of the system changes, it is the preferred quantity. However, it is worth noting that most chemical reactions on the bench are carried out in the most irreversible manner possible by simply mixing reagents in an open container.

5-7. Summary

In this chapter we have introduced some relatively unfamiliar concepts. Although the discussion may seem rather abstract, it is important in the same way that Chapter 2 was important in providing the basis for subsequent utilization of the enthalpy concept. In many ways this present chapter is the crux of thermodynamics. What was presented in previous chapters was, for the most part, not new—it was merely the reduction of familiar notions about the energy concept to an organized and logical body of knowledge. The material in this chapter is also logical, but the logic seems more devious and represents more of a departure from common-sense ideas. The concepts of entropy and free energy have far-reaching implications, and to acquire some understanding of their significance is a major accomplishment.

chapter six

ENTROPY,
CONCENTRATION,
AND CHEMICAL CHANGE

WHETHER a given reaction is feasible can be decided by measuring the potential of an electrochemical cell, as described in Chapter 5. A measured potential for a cell can, in turn, be used to calculate the free energy change which accompanies the reaction in the cell. There are other experimental methods which also give data that lead to free energy calculations. In this chapter a procedure will be discussed that is more widely applicable than cell potentials. The criterion of feasibility remains the same, however: a reaction is feasible if the change is accompanied by a decrease in free energy.

6-1. Concentration Difference and Free Energy

The capacity of a gas always to spread out into a larger volume has been related to probability. A situation quite similar to the spreading of a gas is the spreading of a solute from one solution to another. A concentrated solution inevitably decreases in concentration when placed in contact with a dilute solution. If this mixing occurs spontaneously, a free energy change must be associated with it. How can this be measured?

Rather than mixing the two solutions directly, a concentrated solution and a dilute solution can be used to form an electrochemical cell. An example of such a cell can be constructed by taking two solutions of copper sulfate which differ in concentration. The arrangement is the same as in Fig. 5-1, except that each of the two beakers contains a copper plate and a copper sulfate solution. Such a cell is frequently referred to as a **concentration cell**. If a series of measurements is made for different sets of concentrations, results such as those in Table 6-1 are obtained.

TABLE 6-1. Cell Potential and Concentration Ratio for a $CuSO_4$ Concentration Cell at 25°C*

Conc. A (moles/liter)	Conc. B (moles/liter)	Conc. Ratio (C_A/C_B)	$\mathcal{E}_{max}$ (volts)	ΔG (kcal)
0.98	0.02	49.0	0.049	−2.3
0.95	0.05	19.0	0.039	−1.8
0.90	0.10	9.0	0.027	−1.2
0.80	0.20	4.0	0.018	−0.8
0.70	0.30	2.3	0.010	−0.5
0.50	0.50	1.0	0	0

*Student data, Earlham College.

It is observed that the voltage decreases with decreasing concentration ratio, finally becoming zero when the ratio is exactly 1. The ΔG values in the last column were calculated using Eq. (5-13). Thus a system with a concentration difference also possesses a free energy difference. As material is transferred or rearranged so as to decrease the concentration difference, the free energy difference is reduced. When the concentration difference becomes zero, the free energy difference also becomes zero.

What is the quantitative relationship between concentration ratio and voltage? Using the data in Table 6-1, a plot of

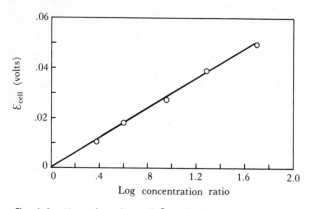

Fig. 6–1. Linear dependence of $\mathcal{E}$ on the logarithm of the concentration ratio, Cu—CuSO$_4$ concentration cell, 25°C.

$\mathcal{E}$ vs. the logarithm of the concentration ratio is found (Fig. 6-1) to give a straight line. (The symbol log refers to logarithms to the base 10). In equation form the potential for this cell can be expressed by

$$\mathcal{E} = \mathbf{k} \log C_A/C_B \tag{6-1}$$

where $\mathbf{k}$ is a proportionality constant and C_A *and* C_B are the concentrations of the two solutions.[1] From the slope of the line in Fig. 6-1, $\mathbf{k}$ is found to be approximately 0.029 volt for the CuSO$_4$ concentration cell at 25°C.

Theoretical arguments lead to the conclusion that the proportionality constant, $\mathbf{k}$, in Eq. (6-1) can be calculated by

[1]More precisely, it is found that $\mathcal{E}$ is proportional to the logarithm of the ratio of *activities* of A and B rather than the ratio of concentrations. The activity of a dissolved ion or molecule may be considered to be a measure of the concentration of that species after correction for interionic or intermolecular attractive forces. In dilute solutions the numerical difference between activity and concentration is small. For simplicity we shall continue to use concentrations in the following discussion, but with the qualification borne in mind that only activities will exactly obey the linear relation in Eq. (6-1).

$$\mathbf{k} = \frac{2.303 \, RT}{nF} \qquad (6\text{-}2)$$

where R is the gas constant (1.987 cal/mole °K), T is the absolute temperature, n is the moles of electrons per mole of reagent, and F is the faraday constant (23,060 cal/volt-mole of electrons). The quantity 2.303 is the factor for conversion from natural logarithms (base e) to common logarithms (base 10). For the Cu–CuSO$_4$ concentration cell described above, $T = 298$°K, $n = 2$, and the calculated value of $\mathbf{k}$ is

$$\mathbf{k} = \frac{2.303 \times 1.987 \times 298}{2 \times 23,060} = 0.0297 \text{ volt}$$

which agrees well with the experimental value. Since 25°C (298°K) is a common reference temperature for laboratory studies and for tabulation of data, it is convenient to combine the quantities 2.303 RT/F into a single constant. For measurements at 25°C, Eq. (6-1) becomes:

$$\mathcal{E} = \frac{0.0591}{n} \log \frac{C_A}{C_B} \qquad (6\text{-}3)$$

Finally, combining Eq. (5-13) with Eqs. (6-1) and (6-2) gives

$$\Delta G = -2.303 RT \log C_A/C_B \qquad (6\text{-}4)$$

When charge flows between the electrodes, copper deposits on one electrode and the copper sulfate concentration decreases around that electrode. At the other electrode copper dissolves and the copper sulfate concentration increases. The net effect of charge flow is a transfer of copper sulfate from one solution to the other.

All the transfer of copper sulfate from a concentrated solution (C_1) to a dilute solution (C_2) could be accompanied by the transfer of useful work out of the system. When the transfer of copper sulfate is arranged so that material goes in the reverse direction, from a dilute to a concentrated solution, all at the same temperature and pressure, work must be put into the system. To carry out this transfer electrically, a potential must be applied which is at least slightly greater than the measured potential for zero current. This means that, although the transfer of copper sulfate from a concentrated to a dilute solution may or may not be used to generate work, there is no escape from the need to supply some minimum amount of work when the transfer is in the reverse direction from a dilute to a concentrated solution.

6-2. Free Energies in Reaction Systems

When a chemical reaction takes place there is a change in the free energy of the system ΔG. This free energy change can be imagined to represent the difference between the individual free energies of the reactants and the individual free energies of the products. Consider, for example, a generalized reaction represented by

$$a\text{A} + b\text{B} \rightarrow c\text{C} + d\text{D}$$

where a moles of A react with b moles of B to form c moles of C plus d moles of D. The free energy change for this reaction is given by

$$\Delta G = cG_\text{C} + dG_\text{D} - aG_\text{A} - bG_\text{B} \tag{6-5}$$

where G_A, G_B, G_C, and G_D represent the free energies of the individual components. Chemists have discovered no suitable way of obtaining these individual free energies; nevertheless it is useful to consider the experimental ΔG as an algebraic function relating products and reactants in the manner implied by Eq. (6-5). A similar situation was encountered in the treatment of enthalpy in Chapter 3.

Eqation (6-5) differs from the corresponding equation for ΔH in one important respect. The enthalpy change for a reaction is not altered significantly by the concentrations of the reactants and products, but the free energy change is. For each component in a reaction system the change in free energy with change in concentration is given by Eq. (6-4). Is it possible to make use of Eq. (6-4) to calculate ΔG for a reaction at one set of concentrations if ΔG is known at another set of concentrations? In particular, it would be desirable to determine a free energy change for some standard set of concentrations so that different systems might be the subject of uniform comparisons. The desired relationship can be obtained by means of an energy cycle; however, first the standard state must be specified.

In Chapter 3 the concept of standard state was introduced to permit the assignment of standard enthalpy changes. The standard state for each substance was defined as the lowest energy modification of that substance at the specified temperature and under a pressure of 1 atm. With free energy calculations, not only must temperature and pressure be specified but also concentration. Therefore the *standard state is extended to include unit concentration for each solute in a solution and 1 atmosphere pressure for each gas present.*[2] With a standard state defined so as to include unit concentration, it is then possible to define the **standard free energy change,** $\Delta G°$, as the change accompanying the conversion of the reactants, each one at unit concentration, to the products, each of which is also at unit concentration. This is clearly a very restrictive condition, but it provides a useful point of reference.

To provide a basis for relating $\Delta G°$ to ΔG at other sets of concentrations, a free energy cycle (Fig. 6-2) can be used.

$$aG°_{\mathrm{A}} \ + \ bG°_{\mathrm{B}} \ \xrightarrow{\ \Delta G°\ } \ cG°_{\mathrm{C}} \ + \ dG°_{\mathrm{D}}$$
$$\uparrow \qquad\qquad \uparrow \qquad\qquad\qquad\quad \downarrow \qquad\qquad \downarrow$$
$$aG_{\mathrm{A}} \ + \ bG_{\mathrm{B}} \ \xrightarrow{\ \Delta G\ } \ cG_{\mathrm{C}} \ + \ dG_{\mathrm{D}}$$

Fig. 6–2

[2] More precisely, the standard state is defined in terms of activity rather than concentration. Numerically the distinction between activity and concentration becomes of major import only for concentrated ionic solutions.

In the bottom part of the diagram, ΔG refers to the reaction of a moles of A at concentration C_A with b moles of B at concentration C_B to form c moles of C at concentration C_C and d moles of D at concentration C_D. As indicated in Fig. 6-2, a free energy change equivalent to ΔG can be produced by a three-step process: (1) conversion of each of the reactants from concentrations C_A and C_B to unit concentration; (2) the reaction of A and B at unit concentration to form C and D also at unit concentration; and (3) the conversion of the products each at unit concentration to concentrations C_C and C_D. Each step of the cycle entails a reversible process carried out at constant pressure and temperature, since only for these conditions is the work transferred a measure of the free energy change.

The free energy change for conversion of a moles of A at concentration C_A to unit concentration is given by Eq. (6-4) as

$$\Delta G_A = a\ 2.3RT \log 1/C_A$$

or, since $a \log X = \log X^a$,

$$\Delta G_A = 2.3RT \log 1/C_A{}^a$$

Corresponding equations may be written for the other components. The complete cycle may then be described by the following equation:

$$\Delta G = 2.3RT \log \frac{1}{C_A{}^a} + 2.3RT \log \frac{1}{C_B{}^b} + \Delta G°$$
$$+ 2.3RT \log \frac{C_C{}^c}{1} + 2.3RT \log \frac{C_D{}^d}{1}$$

Combining the logarithm terms gives finally

$$\Delta G = \Delta G° + 2.3RT \log \frac{C_C{}^c C_D{}^d}{C_A{}^a C_B{}^b} \tag{6-6}$$

Equation (6-6) is a general equation for the free energy change accompanying any chemical reaction. (Eq. (6-4), describing the free energy change for a concentration change can be considered as simply a special case of Eq. (6-6) for which $\Delta G° = 0$.)

The free energy change for a reaction is markedly influenced by concentration changes, as indicated in Eq. (6-6). On the other hand, the enthalpy change for a reaction is not much altered by changes in concentration. A definite energy change, ΔH, is associated with the conversion of a specified number of moles of reactants into products, and it makes relatively little difference how much solvent is present (or in the case of gases, what the total pressure is). The relation between free energy and concentration is, therefore, really an entropy effect. The difference between a mole of solute in a concentrated and in a dilute solution is essentially a difference in the degree of disorder. Therefore, the entropy of a solution depends upon its concentration, and ΔS for a reaction will vary with the relative concentrations of reactants and products. Similarly for reactions involving gases, ΔS will vary with the pressures of the gaseous components.

Equation (6-6) may be used to calculate the free energy change for any desired chemical change at any specified set of concentrations, providing that $\Delta G°$ is known. It becomes important, therefore to ask how $\Delta G°$ can be obtained. One method is by measurement of cell potentials. If Eq. (5-12) is used to substitute for ΔG and $\Delta G°$ in Eq. (6-6) we obtain the following equation:

$$-nF\mathcal{E} = -nF\mathcal{E}° + 2.3RT \log \frac{C_C^c C_D^d}{C_A^a C_B^b}$$

Dividing by $-nF$ gives

$$\mathcal{E} = \mathcal{E}° - 2.3 \frac{RT}{nF} \log \frac{C_C^c C_D^d}{C_A^a C_B^b} \tag{6-7}$$

In order to obtain the standard free energy change for a reaction system that can be set up in an electrochemical cell, all that is necessary is to measure the potential, $\mathcal{E}$, for any known set of concentrations of the reactants and products. Using Eq. (6-7), $\mathcal{E}°$ can be calculated, and from this $\Delta G°$ is obtained using $\Delta G° = -nF\mathcal{E}°$. Eq. (6-7) is known as the **Nernst equation** after the German chemist Walter Nernst. It may be applied to a variety of practical chemical problems, and its utility is enhanced by the fact that electrical measurements are among the most precise that can be made on chemical systems. In particular, the Nernst equation has proved to be a powerful tool in chemical analysis. This equation provides the basis not only for direct determination of ion concentrations by means of electric potential measurements, but also for the interpretation of changes in potential which occur during a titration. Probably the most important application is in the determination of hydrogen ion concentration by means of a pH meter.[3]

6-3. Chemical Equilibrium and Free Energy

If a chemical reaction is allowed to proceed until no further spontaneous change is possible, the system is said to be in a state of chemical equilibrium. It is apparent that the free energy change for the system (i.e., its capacity to do work) must become zero, for if ΔG were some negative value there would still be a tendency for further reaction to occur. But if $\Delta G = 0$, then for this special case Eq. (6-6) becomes

$$\Delta G° = -2.3RT \log \frac{C_C{}^c C_D{}^d}{C_A{}^a C_B{}^b} \qquad (6-8)$$

[3]Discussions of the analytical applications of electrochemical cells are found in most textbooks of analytical chemistry and pysical chemistry.

[4]Strictly speaking it is the quotient of *activities*, rather than concentrations, which is a true constant at a given temperature. We shall ignore this discrepancy, although relatively simple methods are available for converting ionic concentrations to activities for dilute solutions. An excellent discussion of this topic is available in Butler, "Ionic Equilibrium," Addison-Wesley Publishing Co., Reading, Mass., 1964, Chapter 12.

The concentrations in Eq. (6-8) are now the final concentrations of all components when the system has reached a state of equilibrium. For a given chemical system at a specified temperature it is found that the quotient $C_C{}^c C_D{}^d / C_A{}^a C_B{}^b$ always has the same numerical value whenever the system is in a state of chemical equilibrium. This value is called the **equilibrium constant** and is usually denoted by K.[4]

$$K = \frac{C_C{}^c C_D{}^d}{C_A{}^a C_B{}^b} \qquad (6\text{-}9)$$

Combining Eqs. (6-8) and (6-9) gives

$$\Delta G° = -2.3RT \log K \qquad (6\text{-}10)$$

Equation (6-10) is one of the most useful relationships in chemical thermodynamics and it is important to understand its significance. $\Delta G°$ and K refer to quite different states of a system—$\Delta G°$ being the free energy change when all substances are present at unit concentration and K the quotient of the equilibrium concentrations. Yet the logic of the development leads to the conclusion that they are related in a remarkably simple way by Eq. (6-10). Although this has been developed for the specific case of an electrochemical system, we will assume that the relationship between the standard free energy change and the equilibrium constant is perfectly general and applies to all types of chemical systems. Thus concentration measurements in a system at equilibrium can provide the data from which standard free energy changes can be computed.

6-4. Analysis of a Reaction System

As an example of the application of these ideas, let us examine the reaction of iron(II) ion with silver ion in aqueous solution.

$$Fe^{2+}(aq) + Ag^+(aq) \rightarrow Fe^{3+}(aq) + Ag(s)$$

The equilibrium constant for this reaction is found to be approximately 3.0 at 25°C. From this the standard free energy change may be computed.

$$\Delta G°_{298} = -2.3RT \log K$$
$$= -2.3 \times 1.987 \times 298 \times 0.48$$
$$= -0.64 \text{ kcal/mole}$$

Using Eq. (6-6) the relation between free energy change and concentration at 25°C becomes

$$\Delta G = -0.64 + 1.367 \log \frac{C_{Fe^{3+}}}{C_{Fe^{2+}} C_{Ag^+}}$$

Since silver is a separate phase, it is represented by unity in the concentration quotient and need not appear in the calculations.

Let us now consider a series of systems for this reaction such that the total concentration of iron ($Fe^{2+} + Fe^{3+}$) in each one is $2M$ and the concentration of silver ion in each is equal to the Fe^{2+} concentration. Each system also contains some solid silver. For any given set of concentrations (within these limitations) a corresponding free energy change may be calculated. The resulting free energies are plotted in Fig. 6-3 against the concentration of Fe^{3+}. (The data in Fig. 6-3 have been calculated on the assumption—which is only approximately valid—that the activities of the ions are equal to their concentrations.) The curve to the left of the vertical line can be considered to represent the tendency for the reaction to go in the direction indicated by the equation above the curve. With a small concentration of Fe^{3+} present, ΔG is negative and the reaction of Fe^{2+} with Ag^+ is favorable. As the concentration of Fe^{3+} increases, the magnitude of ΔG becomes smaller and the reaction becomes less favorable. At a Fe^{3+} ion concentration of 1.33 M the system is at equilibrium; thus $\Delta G = 0$ and there is no further tendency to react. For systems containing mostly Fe^{3+} and very little Fe^{2+} and

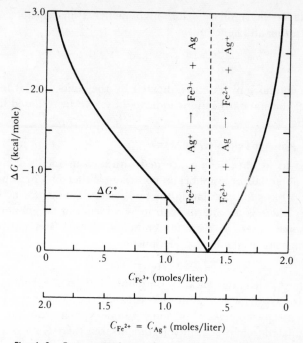

Fig. 6-3. Free energy change as a function of composition for the system Fe^{2+} (aq) + Ag^+ (aq) → Fe^{3+} (aq) + Ag(s), 25°C.

Ag^+ the free energy change favors the reverse reaction, as shown to the right of the vertical line. As the reverse reaction proceeds, ΔG again approaches zero, moving to the left along the curve until finally the equilibrium state is reached. Notice that both arms of the curve rise steeply near the edges of the graph. This means that the corresponding reaction tendency becomes extremely large when *either* set of pure reactants is present.

It is important to observe that the standard state for the system is different from the equilibrium state. At equilibrium

$$\Delta G = 0 \qquad \text{and} \qquad \Delta G° = -2.3RT \log K$$

while for the standard state all components are at unit concentration and hence

$$\log \frac{C_{Fe^{3+}}}{C_{Fe^{2+}} C_{Ag^+}} = 0 \quad \text{and} \quad \Delta G = \Delta G°$$

The equilibrium state is indicated by the solid vertical line, while the standard state is indicated by a vertical dotted line in Fig. 6-3.

6-5. Absolute Entropies; Third Law

So far we have been concerned with measurements of electric potentials or equilibrium constants, either of which provide a basis for calculating the free energy change for a system. There is an alternate strategy which can be employed in some cases. If data for enthalpy change and entropy change are available, the relationship

$$\Delta G = \Delta H - T \Delta S$$

permits calculation of ΔG. Enthalpy changes are comparatively easy to measure, but unfortunately the same is not true for entropy changes. For some simple systems ΔS can be calculated from probability arguments, but there is no way to measure ΔS directly for most chemical changes.

There is, however, a way of obtaining ΔS by a calculation procedure which has become a powerful method in chemical thermodynamics. The calculations are based on two concepts which we shall mention here only briefly.

The first is a postulate known as the **Third Law of Thermodynamics** which is usually stated in the following form: *The entropy of any separate crystalline substance at $0°K$ is zero.* The qualifications "separate" and "crystalline" are necessary because mixtures or noncrystalline solids will still have some degree of disorder even at $0°K$.[5] If, as proposed in the pre-

---

[5]It may be noted that a crystalline element may contain a mixture of nuclei having differing numbers of neutrons and differing spins all randomly arranged even at $0°K$. However, these have no effect on the interpretation of chemical reactions since these contributions to entropy do not alter with temperature change or with chemical reaction.

vious chapter, entropy is a measure of the degree of disorder or randomness within a system, it is reasonable that the entropy will decrease as the temperature goes down. In the limit, at 0°K, all molecular motion ceases and thus for any pure crystalline substance the entropy whould be zero.

The second concept is that change in entropy as a result of temperature change can be calculated from heat capacity data. Using methods of integral calculus, Eq. (6-11) may be derived.

$$\Delta S = \int_{T_1}^{T_2} \frac{C_P}{T} \, dT \qquad (6\text{-}11)$$

The integral in Eq. (6-11) is usually evaluated by a graphical procedure. For example, if C_P/T is plotted as a function of T, the area under the curve from T_1 to T_2 will equal ΔS for this temperature interval. The ΔS so calculated is not the entropy change for a reaction but is the difference between the entropies of a single substance at two temperatures, $\Delta S = S_{T_2} - S_{T_1}$. Suppose now that $T_1 = 0°K$ and $T_2 = 298°K$. According to the third Law, $S_1 = 0$; therefore *the entropy change from 0° to 298°K equals the absolute entropy at 298°K.*

Much research effort in the past 30 years has been devoted to heat capacity measurements over the temperature range from 0 to 300°K for a wide variety of substances. As a result of these efforts, together with entropy changes calculated from ΔG and ΔH data, extensive compilations of absolute entropies are now available in the various reference sources cited in Chapter 3. The absolute entropies of a few substances at 25°C are given in Table 6-2. For purposes of comparison, they have been listed in order of increasing magnitude. Generalizations consistent with the data are: (1) that gases have higher entropies than solids, while liquids lie more or less in between; (2) that hard substances have low entropies and soft substances have high entropies; (3) that the entropy of a substance increases when it is converted from solid to liquid to gas; and (4) that entropy increases with increasing molecular complexity. We shall pursue further the relation between entropy and structure in the next chapter.

TABLE 6-2. Absolute Entropies at 25°C and 1 atm (cal/deg-mole)*

Substance	$S°$	Substance	$S°$
C(diamond)	0.6	$H_2(g)$	31.2
C(graphite)	1.4	$Br_2(l)$	36.4
B(s)	1.6	C(g)	37.8
Fe(s)	6.5	$O_2(g)$	49.0
Na(s)	12.2	$H_2O(g)$	45.1
$H_2O(l)$	16.7	$CO_2(g)$	51.1
NaCl(s)	17.3	$C_2H_6(g)$	54.8
H(g)	27.4	$I_2(g)$	62.3
$I_2(s)$	27.9	$C_3H_8(g)$	64.5

*N.B.S. Circular 500.

With data for the absolute entropies of both reactants and products it is then possible to calculate ΔS for a chemical change.

Example The standard entropy change for the formation of water at 25°C is calculated as follows:

$$\Delta S = S_{H_2O} - S_{H_2} - \tfrac{1}{2}S_{O_2}$$
$$= 16.7 - 31.2 - \tfrac{1}{2}(49.0)$$
$$= -39.0 \text{ cal/mole-deg}$$

6-6. Free Energy and Entropy Data

Three different methods have now been described for obtaining free energy and entropy data for chemical reactions. At constant pressure and temperature free energy changes and entropy changes can each be combined arithmetically using the procedures described in Chapter 3 for enthalpy changes. There are, however, two important differences. First, concentration plays an important role with free energy and entropy; thus concentration must be specified in the standard state for both functions. Second, since it is possible to obtain absolute entropies, these are more often tabulated than are entropies of formation.

The procedures applicable to free energy and entropy calculations may be summarized as follows. (The first four procedures apply also to enthalpy, while items 5 and 6 do not.) (1) Thermochemical equations may be combined algebraically so as to permit the indirect calculation of many free energy and entropy changes. (2) The standard state for each separate substance is taken as the lowest energy form at the specified temperature and a pressure of 1 atm. (3) For convenience in tabulation, data for the free energy of formation of compounds from their elements are used. (4) The free energies and entropies of ionic compounds in aqueous solution are considered to be separable into terms representing the individual ions. (5) The standard state for a substance in solution is taken to be unit concentration (or unit activity). (6) The standard state for the entropy of all separate substances in crystalline form is taken to be 0°K, at which $S° = 0$.

For the formation of a compound from its elements, with each substance in its standard state and all at the same temperature and pressure, the free energy change is called the **standard free energy of formation** and is denoted by $\Delta G_f°$.

The chemistry handbooks, N.B.S. Circular 500, and other reference sources for thermodynamic data give $\Delta G_f°$, as well as $\Delta H_f°$ and $S°$, for many hundreds of compounds. As an interesting exercise in the use of these tables, the reader should try calculating $\Delta G°$ at 25°C for the reaction

$$4NH_3(g) + 3O_2(g) \rightarrow 2N_2(g) + 6H_2O(l)$$

using tabulated free energies of formation. Then using absolute entropies, calculate $\Delta S°$ for this same reaction. Finally, use $\Delta S°$ and $\Delta H°$ (Sec. 3-3) to calculate $\Delta G°$, and compare this with the direct calculation of $\Delta G°$.

For ions in aqueous solution, the convention is used that all thermodynamic properties of $H^+(aq)$ in its standard state at 25°C are equal to zero. As was shown previously for ΔH_f (Sec. 3-4) this then permits calculation of thermodynamic properties for individual ions. The standard reference tables give $\Delta H_f°$, $\Delta G_f°$, and $S°$ for individual ions on the basis of this convention. By adding the quantities for neutral combinations of oppositely charged ions, one obtains appropriate numerical values for salts in aqueous solution.

6-7. Summary

Before proceeding in the next chapter with investigations of some chemical systems, let us summarize the mathematical relationships. The experimental data that can be obtained most readily are (1) enthalpy change from calorimetry, (2) the electrode potential of an electrochemical cell, and (3) the equilibrium constant obtained by standard analytical methods. Not so readily obtained, but still accessible, is the absolute entropy from heat capacity data. The following important relationships have been introduced.

(a) $$\Delta H = Q_p \qquad (2\text{-}7)$$

(b) $$\Delta G = \Delta H - T\Delta S \qquad (5\text{-}8)$$

(c) $$\Delta G = -nF\mathcal{E} \qquad (5\text{-}12)$$

(d) $$\Delta G = \Delta G° + 2.3RT \log \frac{C_C{}^c\, C_D{}^d}{C_A{}^a\, C_B{}^b} \qquad (6\text{-}6)$$

(e) $$\Delta G° = -2.3RT \log K \qquad (6\text{-}10)$$

(f) $$\Delta S = \int_{T_1}^{T_2} \frac{C_p\, dT}{T} \qquad (6\text{-}11)$$

Three major experimental methods are employed for determining the free energy change for a reaction. To obtain calorimetric data, it is necessary to carry out the desired reaction under controlled conditions and to measure the heat transfer. For equilibrium data it is necessary merely to measure the composition of the system in its final state. For electric potentials, the measured quantity is the capacity for change, under conditions such that no change actually takes place. These three techniques are quite different and they measure quite different aspects of a system, yet it is the inter-connection between the various thermodynamic functions—both theoretically and experimentally—which helps to make thermodynamics a powerful tool for the chemist.

With these ideas in mind, let us now turn to data for some typical chemical systems.

chapter seven _____

THERMODYNAMIC
INTERPRETATIONS
OF CHEMICAL REACTIONS

ENTHALPY changes can provide a basis for making choices among alternative reaction pathways. In Chapter 4, enthalpy changes were associated with the structures of chemical reagents for a variety of chemical systems. However, it was shown in Chapter 5 that the direction of change cannot be related solely to energy change; rather, the direction of spontaneous change is determined by a change of entropy as well as of energy. To this end, it was shown that the free energy function provides a convenient criterion for the direction and extent of change.

Direction of change must in some way be linked to structure. It is the purpose of the present chapter to investigate how free energy changes not only govern the direction of spontaneous change but also are related to the structures of the reagents.

The energy-entropy relation for changes at constant temperature and pressure is as follows:

Relation: $$\Delta G \quad = \quad \Delta H \quad - \quad T\Delta S \qquad (7\text{-}1)$$

Interpretation: feasibility of change   bond energies   order–disorder

7-1. Gas Mixtures and Electrochemical Concentration Cells

One of the simplest types of system results from the mixing of two gases. If the gases behave ideally, or nearly so, no appreciable temperature change occurs during mixing, and thus $\Delta H = 0$. But since the mixing occurs spontaneously, the free energy must decrease and the entropy must increase.

For the mixing of one mole of each of two ideal gases at the same temperature and under reversible conditions, it can be shown that

$$\Delta S = +2.76 \text{ cal/deg}$$

From this the free energy change at 25°C may be calculated as follows:

$$\begin{aligned} \Delta G &= \Delta H - T\Delta S \\ &= 0 - 298 \times 2.76 \\ &= -0.822 \text{ kcal} \end{aligned}$$

An electrochemical concentration cell, as described in Sec. 6-1, also represents a system for which $\Delta H = 0$. Both halves of the cell contain the same chemical system; the only difference being in concentration. With dilute solutions, in which charged ions are widely separated, the tendency to react—as reflected in the cell potential—must be due entirely to an entropy increase that accompanies the change from a concentrated to a dilute solution.

7-2. Phase Changes

When a solid substance is converted to a liquid at the normal melting point, the two phases are in equilibrium with each other. A process which is never more than infinitesimally removed from equilibrium is reversible, and the free energy change is zero. Of course, the melting process cannot be strictly reversible and still permit the entire sample to melt in a finite length of time; nevertheless, carefully controlled melting approximates the case of $\Delta G = 0$. But if $\Delta G = 0$, then from Eq. (7-1) it follows that $\Delta H = T\Delta S$.

This implies that any energy absorbed during the melting process increases the entropy and thus also increases the disorder within the system. For the melting of ice at 0°C the situation is

$$\Delta G° = \Delta H° - T\Delta S°$$
$$0 = +1.44 \text{ kcal} - 273° (+5.26 \text{ cal/deg})$$
$$0 = +1.44 - (+1.44) \text{ kcal}$$

At a temperature above the melting point ΔH and ΔS remain nearly constant, but $T\Delta S$ is now larger and thus the spontaneous nature of the reaction is reflected in a negative ΔG or a positive ΔS_{tot}. At 10°C the data for water are:

$$\Delta G° = \Delta H° - T\Delta S°$$
$$= +1.44 \text{ kcal} - 283° (5.26 \text{ cal/deg})$$
$$= +1.44 \text{ kcal} - (+1.49) \text{ kcal}$$
$$= -0.05 \text{ kcal/mole}$$

Vaporization at a temperature close to the normal boiling point of a substance is likewise a situation in which ΔG is close to zero. In this case the heat supplied by the surroundings during vaporization increases the entropy or disorder of the system. For the conversion of water into steam at 100°C and 1 atm pressure the data are:

$$\Delta G° = \Delta H° - T\Delta S°$$
$$= +9.72 \text{ kcal} - 373° (+26.04 \text{ kcal/deg})$$
$$= +9.72 - (+9.72) \text{ kcal}$$
$$= 0$$

Notice however that the enthalpy of vaporization (9.72 kcal) is much larger than the enthalpy of melting (1.44 kcal). This difference may be explained in terms of the relative entropy changes for the two processes. Melting involves a change from an ordered crystal lattice to a jumbled but still fairly compact collection of particles. Vaporization, on the other hand, involves transformation of the still relatively compact liquid into the widely separated and randomly scattered gaseous particles.

One of the older empirical rules in chemistry is Trouton's rule (1884) which states that the enthalpy of vaporization divided by the normal boiling point (in degrees Kelvin) is approximately 21 cal/deg-mole. In light of the concept of entropy, the quantity $\Delta H_{vap}/T$ is simply the entropy of vaporization, ΔS_{vap},

$$\Delta H_{vap}/T = \Delta S_{vap} \approx 21 \text{ cal/deg-mole} \qquad (7\text{-}2)$$

Table 7-1 lists ΔS_{vap} for a few representative substances. It is seen that even for substances with widely differing boil-

TABLE 7-1. Enthalpies and Entropies of Vaporization for Various Substances at Their Normal Boiling Points*

Substance	Boiling Point (°K)	ΔH_{vap} (kcal/mole)	ΔS_{vap} (cal/deg-mole)
N_2	77	1.33	17.2
CH_4	112	1.95	17.5
HCl	188	3.86	20.5
HF	293	1.8	6.1
$CHCl_3$	334	7.02	21.0
H_2O	373	9.72	26.0
Hg	630	13.89	22.1
Mg	1393	31.5	22.6
LiCl	1655	36.0	21.8

*N.B.S. Circular 500.

ing points ΔS_{vap} is fairly constant. This suggests that the change from liquid to gas involves nearly the same change in disorder for all substances. The abnormally high entropy of vaporization for water may be explained in terms of hydrogen bonding; thus liquid water at its boiling point is more highly ordered than most liquids at their boiling points. On the other hand, the low entropy of vaporization for hydrogen fluoride is attributed to extensive intermolecular association in the vapor.

7-3. Free Energy of Formation

One important class of chemical reactions is the formation of compounds from their respective elements. If a compound is to be formed from its elements, how can the formation process best be described? Is the formation reaction feasible or not and what factors control feasibility? To answer these questions, free energies and entropies as well as enthalpies can be determined directly or indirectly for the formation of most substances.

(a) $H_2(g) + \frac{1}{2}O_2(g) \rightarrow H_2O(g)$. For this reaction at 25°C, $\Delta H° = -57.8$ kcal and $\Delta S° = -10.6$ cal/deg. Thus:

$$\Delta H° - T\Delta S° = \Delta G°$$
$$(-57.8) - (-3.2) = (-54.6) \text{ kcal}$$

The large negative free energy change indicates that the formation reaction is highly feasible, but it is evident that the favorable free energy change is due to a highly favorable enthalpy change and a slightly unfavorable entropy change. The negative ΔS is reasonable for a reaction involving rupture of $1\frac{1}{2}$ bonds and the making of 2 bonds per H_2O molecule formed.

(b) $C(s) + 2H_2(g) \rightarrow CH_4(g)$. For this reaction at 25°C the appropriate data are:

$$\Delta H° - T\Delta S° = \Delta G°$$
$$(-17.9) - (-5.8) = (-12.1) \text{ kcal}$$

The enthalpy change is much smaller than that for water, because of the large sublimation enthalpy of solid carbon. The negative entropy change suggests that the arrangement of carbon and hydrogen atoms within methane molecules provides a more highly ordered state than does a system of hydrogen molecules and the extended crystal lattice of solid carbon. In summary, the free energy change for the formation reaction is only about 2/3 as favorable as the enthalpy change alone would indicate.

(c) $\frac{1}{2}N_2(g) + \frac{3}{2}H_2(g) \rightarrow NH_3(g)$. At 25°C the appropriate data are as follows:

$$\Delta H° - T\Delta S° = \Delta G°$$
$$(-11.0) - (-7.0) = (-4.0) \text{ kcal}$$

The relatively small favorable enthalpy change and the unfavorable entropy change combine to give a free energy change which is only slightly favorable. The entropy decrease is reasonable in view of the relative numbers of bonds in the reactants and product. The small magnitude of the enthalpy change is a consequence of the exceptionally large bond enthalpy for elemental nitrogen.

It is interesting to note that the compounds, CH_4, NH_3, and H_2O constitute an isolectronic series of molecules. Each molecule contains 10 electrons, but they differ in the number and arrangement of their nuclei. The variations in the thermodynamic functions within this series are due in part to the arrangement of nuclei, but to a larger degree to the differences in elemental carbon, nitrogen and oxygen.

One important qualification must be borne in mind in interpreting the above data. Thermodynamic values given in each case are the standard state changes. They refer to a reaction under the particular condition in which all reactants and products are simultaneously present at unit concentration or 1 atm pressure. For the NH_3 reaction in particular, it should be evident that $\Delta G°$ is so close to zero that changes in the concentrations of the reactants and products will quite significantly alter the magnitude and even change the sign of ΔG.

7-4. Formation of Hydrogen Halides

It is instructive to examine data for a related series of substances within a family of the periodic table. Data for the formation reactions of the hydrogen halides are given in Table 7-2. Looking first at the enthalpy changes at 298°K, the formation reaction becomes less exothermic going from HF to HI, and is in fact endothermic for HI. Such a trend is consistent with the increasing size of the halogen kernel, which means less attraction between the halogen atom and the hydrogen atom. With entropy, however, the trend is in the opposite direction. The jump in $\Delta S°$ at 298°K between

TABLE 7-2. Thermodynamic Data for the Formation of the Hydrogen Halides at 298°K and 500°K Under a Pressure of 1 atm*

Compound	$\Delta H°$ (kcal/mole)	$\Delta S°$ (cal/deg-mole)	$\Delta G°$ (kcal/mole)
	Reaction at 298°K		
HF (g)	−64.5	1.7	−65.0
HCl (g)	−22.0	2.4	−22.7
HBr (g)	− 8.7	13.6	−12.7
HI (g)	6.3	19.9	0.4
	Reaction at 500°K		
HF (g)	−64.6	1.5	−65.3
HCl (g)	−22.1	2.0	−23.1
HBr (g)	−12.5	2.1	−13.6
HI (g)	− 1.3	2.1	− 2.4

*J.A.N.A.F. Thermochemical Tables.

HCl and HBr may seem inconsistent with the similarity of $\Delta S°$ for HF and HCl. However, in their standard states at 298°K elemental bromine and iodine are liquid and solid, respectively, while elemental fluorine and chlorine are gases.

It is possible to compute the comparable thermodynamic quantities at higher temperatures where both bromine and iodine are gases in their standard states. As an example, data for the formation reactions at 500°K, with all components in the gas phase, are assembled in Table 7-2. Although the free energy changes show the same pattern at each of the two temperatures, the data for ΔS show different patterns. At 500°K ΔS is almost the same—about 2 cal/deg-mole—for the four halides, while at 298°K ΔS is about 2 cal/deg-mole for HF and HCl, but more than six times as large for HBr and HI. Therefore, the positive free energy of formation for HI at 298°K, in contrast to the negative free energies for the other hydrogen halides, is accounted for by the greater stability of solid iodine compared to gaseous iodine.

7-5. Hydrocarbon Formation

As a final example of formation reactions, data are assembled in Table 7-3 for the formation of a homologous series of hydrocarbons. In this case all compounds are formed from the same two elements and the differences are the number of nuclei, electrons, and bonds in the various compounds.

TABLE 7-3. Thermodynamic Data for Hydrocarbon Formation at 25°C and 1 atm*

Compound	Formula	ΔH_f° (kcal/mole)	ΔS° (cal/deg-mole)	ΔG_f° (kcal/mole)
Methane	$CH_4(g)$	-17.89	-19.3	-12.14
Ethane	$C_2H_6(g)$	-20.24	-41.5	-7.86
Propane	$C_3H_8(g)$	-24.80	-64.4	-5.61
n-Butane	$C_4H_{10}(g)$	-29.81	-87.4	-3.75
n-Pentane	$C_5H_{12}(g)$	-35.00	-110.8	-1.96
n-Hexane	$C_6H_{14}(g)$	-39.96	-134.5	$+0.05$
n-Heptane	$C_7H_{16}(g)$	-44.89	-157.6	$+2.09$
n-Octane	$C_8H_{18}(g)$	-49.82	-181.0	$+4.14$
n-Nonane	$C_9H_{20}(g)$	-54.74	-204.3	$+6.18$
n-Decane	$C_{10}H_{22}(g)$	-59.67	-227.7	$+8.23$

*N.B.S. Circular 461.

In Table 7-3, the enthalpies of formation not only are all negative, but they become more negative as the number of carbon nuclei increases. Energetically it might be concluded that each hydrocarbon is more stable than the preceding one, as a result of the formation of an additional C—C bond and two C—H bonds. The entropy changes, however, become increasingly negative for each additional CH_2 group, so that the free energy change is negative for the first five compounds, nearly zero for hexane, and becomes increasingly positive for the compounds below hexane in the table. We must conclude, therefore, that the larger hydrocarbons are thermodynamically unstable at room temperature with respect to carbon and hydrogen, because the bonds simply are not strong enough to support the degree of organization required when many atoms are assembled in one molecule. Thus the larger hydrocarbons cannot be made by direct synthesis from the elements. Any successful synthesis must be from other compounds or at different conditions of temperature and pressure.

7-6. Ionic Reactions

In order to calculate entropy and free energy changes accompanying ionic reactions it is helpful to have data available for individual ions. By arbitrarily assigning the number zero to all thermodynamic properties of the aqueous hydrogen ion, a self-consistent set of data for individual ions can be obtained (Sec. 6-9).

Consider, for example, the neutralization reaction,

$$HCl + NaOH \rightarrow NaCl + H_2O$$

In dilute aqueous solution this reaction is essentially described by

$$H^+(aq) + OH^-(aq) \rightarrow H_2O(l)$$

The enthalpy change for this reaction at 25°C was shown earlier (Sec. 3-5) to be negative, with $\Delta H°_{298} = -13.36$ kcal/mole. Calculation of the entropy change gives

$$\begin{aligned} \Delta S° &= S°_{H_2O} - S°_{H^+} - S°_{OH^-} \\ &= 16.72 - 0 - (-2.52) \\ &= 19.24 \text{ cal/deg-mole} \end{aligned}$$

This result seems surprising at first glance. The reaction in dilute solution involves essentially the combination of $H^+(aq)$ and $OH^-(aq)$ ions to form $H_2O(l)$. Surely such a combination should produce greater order and thus lower entropy; yet the calculated entropy change is positive! An explanation can be based on the nature of the hydrated ions. When neutralization takes place, water molecules initially bound to the ions by electrostatic attraction are released, and thus the reaction is represented more completely by

$$H^+ \cdot x H_2O + OH^- \cdot y H_2O \rightarrow (x + y + 1) H_2O$$

The entropy increase therefore suggests that the water of hydration around the ions is more organized than liquid water.

Finally, the free energy change for the neutralization reaction at 25°C may be calculated as follows:

$$\begin{aligned}
\Delta G° &= \Delta H° - T \Delta S° \\
&= -13.36 \text{ kcal} - (298°K \times 19.24 \text{ cal/deg-mole}) \\
&= -13.36 - 5.74 \\
&= -19.10 \text{ kcal/mole}
\end{aligned}$$

(The reader may verify for himself that an identical value for $\Delta G°$ is obtained if free energies of formation are used, rather than enthalpy and entropy data.)

From the value of $\Delta G°$ the equilibrium constant may be calculated.

$$\begin{aligned}
\log K &= -\frac{\Delta G°}{2.3 RT} \\
&= -\frac{-19{,}100}{2.3 \times 1.987 \times 298} = 14
\end{aligned}$$

or

$$K = 10^{14}$$

This equilibrium constant is the reciprocal of the familiar ion product constant for the dissociation of water at 25°C.

As another example of ionic reactions, consider the formation of an insoluble compound. In Chapter 5 the reaction between calcium chloride and sodium carbonate,

$$CaCl_2 (aq) + Na_2CO_3 (aq) \rightarrow CaCO_3 (s) + 2NaCl (aq)$$

was given as an example of a reaction which occurs spontaneously, even though the enthalpy change is positive ($\Delta H°_{298} = +2.95$ kcal/mole). The essential ionic reaction in dilute aqueous solution is

$$Ca^{2+} (aq) + CO_3^{2-} (aq) \rightarrow CaCO_3 (s)$$

and thus the entropy change for the system at 25°C can be calculated most simply as follows:

$$\Delta S^\circ_{sys} = S^\circ_{CaCO_3} - S^\circ_{Ca^{2+}} - S^\circ_{CO_3^{2-}}$$
$$= 22.2 - (-13.2) - (-12.7)$$
$$= 48.1 \text{ cal/deg-mole}$$

The entropy change in the system is apparently quite favorable for this reaction even though the reaction results in formation of a highly ordered solid compound. Again, this positive ΔS is presumably due to the release of water of hydration from the ions and a consequent increase in disorder. Calculation of ΔG° gives

$$\Delta G^\circ = \Delta H^\circ - T\Delta S^\circ$$
$$= +2.95 - 14.33$$
$$= -11.38 \text{ kcal/mole}$$

It appears, therefore, that the free energy change for the precipitation reaction is favorable at constant temperature, but that this free energy change is a composite of a large favorable entropy change for the system and a small unfavorable enthalpy change.

It is instructive to examine the corresponding data for precipitation of the rest of the series of Group II carbonates. Table 7-4 summarizes the relevant data with the changes shown graphically in Fig. 7-1. For each of these compounds ΔS° is highly favorable for the precipitation reaction, but

TABLE 7-4. Thermodynamic Data for Precipitation of the Group II Carbonates from Aqueous Solution, 25°C and 1 atm*

Compound	ΔH° (kcal/mole)	$T\Delta S^\circ$ (kcal/mole)	ΔG° (kcal/mole)
$MgCO_3(s)$	+6.	+17.	-11.
$CaCO_3(s)$	+2.9	+14.3	-11.4
$SrCO_3(s)$	+0.8	+13.3	-12.5
$BaCO_3(s)$	-1.0	+11.0	-12.0

*N.B.S. Circular 500.

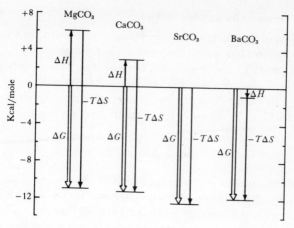

Fig. 7–1. Thermodynamic representation for the precipitation reactions of the Group II carbonates, 25°C.

the magnitude of $\Delta S°$ decreases steadily from $MgCO_3$ to $BaCO_3$. For all but $BaCO_3$, $\Delta H°$ is positive and therefore unfavorable. However, the trends in $\Delta S°$ and $\Delta H°$ are in the opposite direction, so that $\Delta G°$ remains nearly constant.

A reasonable explanation for the decreasing magnitude of $T\Delta S°$ going from magnesium to barium is the decreasing extent of hydration of the metal ions due to a decreasing charge/radius ratio. The variation in $\Delta H°$ is the net result of two opposing factors: decreasing magnitude of the hydration enthalpies of the metal ions and decreasing magnitude of the lattice enthalpy of the solid carbonates (Sec. 4-2). Both these factors may be attributed to the decreasing charge/radius ratio. The decrease in hydration enthalpy is the slightly larger factor; thus ΔH for the precipitation reaction becomes less positive from magnesium to strontium and slightly negative for barium. Therefore all the factors which must be taken into account for thermodynamic interpretation of this set of reactions can be explained ultimately on the basis of the relative sizes of the metal ions.

7-7. Temperature and Feasibility

Most of the discussion of the feasibility of chemical change in a system has been confined to one temperature, 25°C. Data at 25°C are important because the vast majority of chemical reactions are carried out at temperatures not far from this value. Nevertheless, it is of interest to examine the effect which variations in temperature have on reaction feasibility. Eq. (7-1)

$$\Delta G = \Delta H - T\Delta S$$

provides a means of analyzing the effect.

In Sec. 3-6 ΔH for a given reaction was shown to be nearly constant, even over a wide temperature range. This is reasonable, since a fixed amount of energy is associated with the formation and dissociation of each of the bonds involved in a given chemical reaction, regardless of the temperature at which the change occurs. Furthermore, it is reasonable to assume that ΔS for a give reaction does not change greatly with temperature because approximately the same change in the degree of disorder will be involved when the reaction takes place, whatever the temperature. But if ΔS is nearly constant, then the quantity $T\Delta S$ will become progressively larger in magnitude as the temperature increases. This means that for a given energy transfer the entropy change in the surroundings—either positive or negative—will be smaller as the temperature rises. The entropy of the surroundings changes because of heat transferred into or out of the system ($Q/T = \Delta H/T$ at constant pressure); and as the temperature at which the transfer takes place increases, the relative change in the disorder of the surroundings will become smaller.

At low temperatures, $T\Delta S$ will be small in magnitude and therefore ΔH will be the dominant term contributing to ΔG. Even at 298°K, ΔH is the dominant term for most reactions, as seen in the preceding sections of this chapter. On the other hand, at high temperatures—for example, above a thousand degrees—$T\Delta S$ is large in magnitude and therefore tends to be the dominant term contributing to ΔG.

In summary, at sufficiently low temperatures the reaction feasibility is always controlled in sign and magnitude by the enthalpy change, ΔH, while at sufficiently high temperature it is always controlled by the sign and magnitude of the entropy change, ΔS. Both ΔH and ΔS result from structural changes within the system; yet they represent quite different aspects of the change, and play different roles in their effect on feasibility.

Figure 7–2 presents data for the H_2–O_2–H_2O system from low temperature up to 6000°K. ΔH for the formation reac-

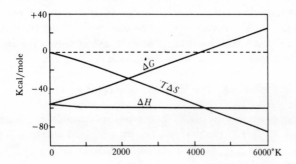

Fig. 7–2. Thermodynamic data from 0° to 6000°K for the system $H_2(g) + \frac{1}{2}O_2(g) \rightarrow H_2O(g)$ at 1 atm. ("J.A.N.A.F. Thermochemical Tables," The Dow Chemical Co., Midland, Mich., 1961.)

tion is nearly constant at about −58 kcal over the entire temperature range. Except at low temperatures, ΔS is nearly constant at −14 cal/deg over the whole range, so that $T\Delta S$ increases in magnitude in an approximately linear manner. At temperatures approaching zero, $T\Delta S$ also approaches zero; thus ΔG is determined almost completely by ΔH and the formation reaction is highly feasible.

On the other hand, at high temperatures $T\Delta S$ becomes a large negative quantity which more than offsets the negative ΔH. Above 4000°K with all components at 1 atmosphere pressure ΔG is positive and water decomposes spontaneously into hydrogen and oxygen. This is not a surprising conclusion. Regardless of the strength of the bonds in a molecule, increasing the temperature increases the kinetic energy of the system, and thus creates a progressively greater tendency toward a more chaotic state for the system. At sufficiently high temperatures all bonds will break, even those within elemental gas molecules.

The formation of water is a reaction for which ΔS is negative and therefore it becomes less feasible at high temperatures. Reactions which occur with a positive entropy change, on the other hand, become more feasible at high temperatures. One example of such a reaction is the industrially important "water gas" reaction,

$$C(s) \quad + \quad H_2O(g) \quad \rightarrow \quad CO(g) \quad + \quad H_2(g)$$

An energy-temperature diagram for this reaction is shown in Fig. 7-3. ΔH is nearly constant at $+30$ kcal over the whole range, while ΔS_{sys} for this reaction is $+32$ kcal/deg over most of the range. At low temperature ΔG is positive, as implied by ΔH. As the temperature increases $T\Delta S$ becomes larger, so that at approximately 1000°K, $T\Delta S$ and ΔH are equal in magnitude. Above this temperature ΔG is negative and the reaction becomes feasible. Thermodynamic analysis of the system therefore shows that a temperature of at least 1000°K is necessary for this reaction to take place to an appreciable extent at 1 atm.

Notice that in both of the examples ΔH and $T\Delta S$ have the same sign over the whole temperature range. This is generally the case. A low energy state is generally a

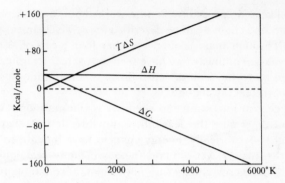

Fig. 7–3. Thermodynamic data from 0° to 6000°K for the system $H_2O(g) + C(s) \rightarrow CO(g) + H_2(g)$ at 1 atm. ("J.A.N.A.F. Thermochemical Tables," The Dow Chemical Co., Midland, Mich., 1961.)

highly ordered state; therefore a reaction which results in a state of greater order for the system (ΔS negative) is almost always exothermic (ΔH negative). Conversely, reactions which result in greater disorder (ΔS positive) must absorb energy from the environment; therefore ΔH is positive. The only important exceptions to this are ionic reactions in aqueous solution, where the organizing effect of the ions on the solvent molecules plays a significant role.

7-8. Summary

In this brief volume we have tried to follow a logical—though somewhat circuitous—path from chemical change, to energy, to structure, to entropy, and finally to the feasibility of change. Central to the entire investigation has been the observation that most chemical changes in the laboratory are accompanied by changes in the environment—as if the chemical system and its surroundings were coupled.

The conservative aspect of the coupling has been labeled energy. Energy is imagined to be an immaterial entity which is transferred without loss. As a consequence of this thinking a bookkeeping procedure can be worked out, and an energy or enthalpy change can be described for every chemical reaction. Through analysis of energy change in terms of alternative reaction pathways we have seen that some notion can be gained as to the factors controlling the magnitude and the sign of the energy change.

Of central importance to chemists is the question "What factors determine the feasibility and direction of chemical change?" Historically, energy changes were thought to provide the answer; yet we find there are many reactions for which the energy changes do not give an adequate explanation. Consideration of the processes of energy transfer, therefore, led to the introduction of a nonconservative property called entropy. Although defined in terms of the experimental variables heat, work and temperature, entropy changes are also identified conceptually with changes in the degree of order within a system and its surroundings. Every chemical reaction and indeed every spontaneous change of any kind proceeds so that there is an increase in total entropy when system and surroundings are considered together. For many reactions the system itself decreases in entropy, but this decrease is then always associated with a heat transfer to the surroundings sufficient to raise the entropy of the surroundings more than the system decreases in entropy. To describe the feasibility of change in terms only of the system in its initial and final states, a new function called free energy was introduced. Free energy change is a function of both energy change and entropy change, so that if a reaction occurs with an unfavorable energy change, the entropy change of the system must be sufficiently favorable to more than offset the unfavorable energy change.

In this final chapter, knowledge of energy and entropy has been applied to the investigation of several chemical systems. Phase changes, compound formation reactions and ionic reactions in aqueous solution, all permit significant interpretations to be made when subjected to complete thermodynamic analysis. Such an analysis of energy and entropy changes provides a basis for choosing among alternative explanations of why some reactions occur and others do not. Thermodynamics is therefore a most useful interpretive device for chemists as they seek to understand the nature of chemical reactions.

INDEX